CHRISTIAN EDUCATION LIBRARY
DO NOT REMOVE

SIX O'CLOCK SAINTS

SIX O'CLOCK
SAINTS

By
JOAN WINDHAM
WITH ILLUSTRATIONS BY
MARIGOLD HUNT

NEW YORK
SHEED & WARD INC.

249.9
W 749

145223

PRINTED IN THE U. S. A.

COPYRIGHT 1934
BY SHEED AND WARD, INC.

PREFACE FOR GROWN-UPS

THESE Stories have been written with the object of making Children familiar with the Saints as Ordinary People to whom Interesting Things have happened.

The Six-year-old is easily bored by " good " stories, and I have tried to avoid this pitfall. Later on, when they are older, and they read " devotional " Lives of the Saints, I hope that they will remember these Special Stories and will say to themselves : " Oh ! That was the man who did such and such a thing. He can't have been so bad after all ! "

I tried hard to include St. Philip Neri, but, although he was extraordinarily helpful about the others, he simply would not be done himself.

Adding the dates of the Feasts may seem to be superfluous, but should one of them coincide with Somebody's Birthday it will make that story so much more Special.

J. W.

ORCHARD STABLES,
WARGRAVE,
BERKS.

CONTENTS

SIX O'CLOCK SAINTS

SIX O'CLOCK SAINTS

A LEGEND OF THE FLIGHT INTO EGYPT

WHEN Our Lord was nearly two years old He was living with Our Lady and St. Joseph in their house in Bethlehem. (It was the same house they were in when the Three Wise Men came to see them, bringing presents to the Baby Lord.)

Now, King Herod was very, very angry when he heard that there was a new King born in Bethlehem. *He* wanted to be the most Special and Important King in the Land, and if there were *two* kings they would have to share Importances, and he didn't want to do that. So he Summoned his Councillors and he said :

" As those Three Wise Men haven't come back to tell me where the new baby King is, I suppose they must have gone home another way. So do any of you know where he lives, because I want him Killed ? When I asked the Wise Men they *said* Bethlehem, but now they have tricked me once, that might be a trick too."

None of the Councillors knew *exactly* where Our Lady and St. Joseph lived, but one of them said :

" My brother heard the Three Wise Men talking about Bethlehem, Your Majesty, so I suppose they *must* be somewhere near there."

" The only Thing to Do," said horrible King Herod, " is to kill *all* the baby boys that are Two Years Old and Less than Two Years Old, because He is *sure* to be one of them, and then I can still be the most Important King."

The Councillors thought this was Rather a Bad Idea, but they didn't say so in case King Herod had them killed too ; like he did, if people didn't always agree with him.

So Herod sent for one of his Officers.

" Take your Soldiers," he said, " and go to Bethlehem and kill *every* little boy there is who is Two Years Old or Less than Two Years Old. It doesn't matter who they are, rich or poor, kill them all and start first thing to-morrow morning."

That night, while the soldiers were Packing Up ready to go to Bethlehem, God sent an Angel to St. Joseph, who was asleep, and the Angel said :

" Get up *quickly* and take Our Lady and the baby Jesus and go to Egypt ! Herod is sending his soldiers to kill all the little boys to-morrow, so go *now*, and stay there until I come and tell you that it is all right again."

So, in the Middle of the Night, St. Joseph went and woke up Our Lady, and, while she was packing up a few clothes and some food (they couldn't take very much because of carrying it), and dressing the baby Jesus, he went out to the stable to get his big Donkey. It was a very big Donkey, like a pony, not like the little sea-side ones, and it had a dark-brown stripe all the way down its back from its head to its tail, and its name was Pharaoh because it came from Egypt.

St. Joseph usually called it Flopears because its ears were so big and floppy, and Our Lady called it Softears because they were so soft to stroke.

Well, St. Joseph woke up Pharaoh (who wondered why they were going out in the Middle of the Night) and put on the saddle so that Our Lady could ride

when she got tired. Then he hung two big baskets, one each side of the saddle, to put the food and clothes in. Then he led Pharaoh round to the door and told him to wait a minute while he went in to help carry out the bundles for the baskets.

" Are you ready ? " he asked Our Lady, " because we *must* hurry ; it is nearly to-morrow, when the soldiers are coming."

" I'm just coming," said Our Lady, and she popped

two wooden animals that St. Joseph had made for
Jesus into the basket just as St. Joseph was carrying
it downstairs. She picked up Jesus and wrapped a
shawl round him and hurried down, and found St.
Joseph putting rags round Pharaoh's hooves so that
he would not make a noise on the stony street.

They walked all the night and by the morning they

were miles and miles away from Bethlehem and on
the way to Egypt. It takes four days to walk from
Bethlehem to the nearest bit of Egypt, so they had to
sleep on the way. Once they came to a Shepherd's
Hut on the side of a hill, and the Shepherd let them
spend a night there, but mostly they had to walk over
Hot Dusty Desert. St. Joseph was carrying their
water in a goat-skin and he was getting very worried
about whether they would have enough water to last
them out, because it was *so* hot, and they kept getting
so thirsty, and Pharaoh drank such a lot at once,
when it was his turn.

At last they saw two Palm Trees sticking up out of the sand.

" Good ! " said St. Joseph. " There must be some water there or the trees wouldn't grow. Now we can rest in the shade, and I will fill up the goat-skin."

Pharaoh pricked up his floppy ears and began to trot, because *he* wanted to rest in the shade, too.

But, under the Palm Trees, there was a Band of Robbers, who had got there first ! They were all asleep (because they had been Robbing all night), except the Two Youngest, who were Keeping Guard. The names of these two were Dysmas and Gestas.

When Dysmas and Gestas saw Our Lady and St. Joseph coming towards them, Gestas said :

" Look ! Let's Rob these people ! They've got some big bundles and a strong donkey. If we take their water, too, they will die of thirst and then they can't tell anyone. Let's wake the Others and make an Ambush."

(An Ambush is when people hide behind things and Pounce Out on you.)

" No, don't let's," said Dysmas. " They don't look very Rich and we've Robbed quite a lot of people lately, and the Lady looks very tired. Let's Warn them instead."

" Well ! " said Gestas, " I *do* call that a silly idea ! What's the good of being a Robber if you don't Rob ? "

" Well, if I give you my share of last night's Robbings, will you let them go ? " asked Dysmas.

" All right, I suppose so," said Gestas.

So Dysmas ran out to meet Our Lady and St.

Joseph and Warned them. Our Lady thanked him very much and St. Joseph said :

" We are very short of water. Do you think you could fill our goat-skin for us without waking the Others ? "

Dysmas went to fill it, and when he came back he looked at the Baby Jesus and said :

" I love your Baby, he is the sweetest one I have ever seen. What is his name ? "

And Our Lady said :

" His name is Jesus, and some day He will reward you Himself for what you have done for us to-day."

Dysmas couldn't think what she meant. " I don't suppose I shall ever see them again," he said to himself as he watched them going out of sight.

But, when Our Lord was grown-up and was Crucified, you remember the two Thieves who were crucified at the same time ? Well, one was Gestas and the other was Dysmas ! And Dysmas was the one who asked Our Lord not to forget him, and Our Lord said to him :

" *To-day* you shall come to Heaven with Me." So he had a very Special reward, after all, didn't he ? because he was the *only* person (except Gestas, the Bad Thief, who doesn't count because he wasn't looking) in the Whole World who has died looking at a *Real* Crucifix, not just a statue of one. He hung on his Cross, looking at God Himself crucified on *His* Cross, and so he forgot his own pain and just loved Jesus until he died, and then went to Him in Heaven. And if you can think of a more perfectly lovely way to die than that I would like you to let me know.

When the Holy Family got to Egypt, they found a very cheap house to live in at a place called Heliopolis, near Cairo. It had to be a cheap one because St. Joseph had earned all his money in his Carpenter's Shop, and they'd had to leave that behind ! (I wonder who looked after it for them ?) Anyway, Our Lady had brought the Gold and the Frankincense and the Myrrh that the Wise Men had given to the Baby Lord, so she sold these (they were very valuable) and then they had enough money to live on. The Wise Men would have been very glad if they had known how useful their presents had been.

They had only been in Egypt a few months when the Angel came back and said :

" It is all right now, King Herod is dead, so you can go home again."

So they packed up all their things once more ! We do not know how they went back. There wasn't such a hurry this time, so perhaps they went back by Sea, in a Boat. It would have been nicer for them, not so hot and dusty as the Desert, and no Robbers and Ambushes and things. But when St. Matthew was writing about it, he didn't say.

But they never got back to Bethlehem after all ! Because on the way they heard that King Herod's son Archelaus, who was now King, was just as horrible as his father, so it would be safer to live far away from him ! So St. Joseph said to God :

" Where is a good place to go that will be safe for Jesus and Mary ? "

And God said that he'd better go to Galilee, because another of Herod's sons ruled there (like the Prince

of Wales rules in Wales), and this other son, called
Herod Antipas, didn't bother much about his subjects.

So they went and lived in a town called Nazareth,
in Galilee, and St. Joseph had a new shop to be a
Carpenter in, and he made more little wooden Birds
and Animals for the little Jesus to play with until He
grew big enough to learn to be a Carpenter Himself.

Now, there is a Special Day belonging to this Story,
too, and I will give you three Guesses whom it belongs
to. Our Lady? No. St. Joseph? No. Not even
Dysmas the Good Thief, because he has his own Special
Day. Well, it belongs to all those little boys who were
killed in Bethlehem. What Lucky little boys they
were, weren't they? They had very little time to
wait before Heaven was opened for them, and they
had no chance of Denying Our Lord, as some of
them might have done if they had grown up and
been there when He was Crucified. And they were
Martyrs, too, because they died for Our Lord's sake,
although they couldn't help it. So they are called
the Holy Innocents, because they were too little to
sin, and their Special Day is the 28th of December,
quite near Christmas, when Our Lord is little, too.

ST. LONGINUS

ONCE upon a time there was a Roman Soldier who loved fighting. He had a round shining shield, and a big shining helmet, and he carried a long shining spear. Round his waist was a leather belt with a scabbard to keep his sword in, and on his feet were sandals that laced all the way up to his knees. His name was Longinus and he was a Centurion.

A Centurion is a soldier who is the Captain of a Hundred Men (like a *century* is a hundred years), and Longinus used to march out at the head of his hundred men, very Stiff and Proud, and Lead them into Battle. They nearly always won, because Longinus was so good at being a Centurion.

Longinus lived in Jerusalem (which really belonged to the Jews, but the Romans had conquered the Jews and so they were the Grand People who did the Ruling). He was very tall and strong, and the only thing that bothered him was that he couldn't see as well as other people and things far away always looked faint and misty. Nowadays he would have had spectacles, but the Romans didn't have them.

Well, one evening the Roman Governor who governed the Jews said to Longinus :

" I wish you'd take some of your men up to the Jewish High Priest's house ; there is a Jewish prisoner there. Bring him here to the Barracks and do not let him escape. He is a Traitor." (A Traitor is someone who says he is More Important than the King.)

Longinus saluted and said he would go there at once. So he took four of his Hundred Men and went off. But the Prisoner did not even try to escape on the way back, and Longinus was rather sorry about that because he had heard that this prisoner had been a great Bother in the Town, making crowds and things, and people said that he was a King and More Important than Cæsar-who-was-King-of-the-Romans. Now Cæsar was the Most Important King there was, so it was an Imprisoning Thing to pretend you were grander than he was. Besides if the prisoner had escaped it would have been an Exciting Thing to capture him again. But he just walked along and Longinus was very disappointed.

Now the Barracks was a big place where all the Roman soldiers lived ; and because it was so late and after supper they took the prisoner into their big Hall where all the soldiers were to wait until the morning.

"Here's a Jewish prisoner ! " shouted the soldiers who were in the Hall. "Let's have some fun with him ! " And while Longinus and his four men were having a late supper which had been kept hot for them, the others tied the prisoner's hands behind his back and blindfolded him. Then they all took it in turns to hit him in the face as hard as they could and tried to make him guess who it was. Soon they got tired of this game and one of them said :

"Let's pretend he is a King ! He *said* he was Grander than Cæsar."

So they made him a crown out of a prickly plant that people used for hedges, and pressed it down on his head so that the thorns stuck in all round. Then they put a purple horse-rug, from the Barracks stable, round him for a King's cloak, and then they all laughed at him, and stood round and pointed! They got worse and worse, pushing him, knocking him into things (you remember that he was still blindfolded), and running him up and down the room. The prisoner never said anything at all, but he was very badly hurt.

At last Longinus finished his supper and stood up. He put on his helmet, straightened his sword and turned round.

" Now then, you men ! " he said crossly, " That's enough ! Don't make him lame ! He's got to go and see the Governor in the morning, and I don't want to have to get out a special horse to carry him."

So the soldiers stopped, but they didn't take off the crown or the horse-rug, neither did they untie his hands. Then Longinus took him and shut him up in a Prisoners' Cell for the night, and he locked the door with a jangling key.

" Try and go to sleep," he said, " nothing more will happen until the morning."

But he forgot that you can't lie down and go to sleep with your hands tied behind you, or even sit with your head leaning against the wall if you have thorns round your head. So the prisoner, who was very hurt and tired, just had to stand and wait until the morning. He was very lonely and hungry.

In the morning, Longinus unlocked the door of the

Prisoners' Cell, hurried in and took the prisoner to see the Governor at once, as he was rather late, having overslept. He had forgotten to give him any breakfast; he had only *just* had time to have his own. After a very unfair trial the prisoner was Condemned to Death for pretending he was a King. Now, in those days, all the prisoners who were Condemned to Death were not hanged, neither did they have their heads cut off. They were usually nailed by their hands and feet onto a wooden cross, in the morning, and then left all day until they were dead. Sometimes they didn't die until the next day, so you can see what a horrible way it was.

This time there were two other prisoners who had to be crucified at the same time, for stealing things from the Governor's house, so the three men were marched away by the four soldiers, one for each prisoner, and one to give orders, and Longinus went back to the Barracks. He was very busy all day getting ready for a Battle. He had to see to all his own things and then he had to go to all his Hundred Soldiers and see that *their* things were clean and tidy and their spears sharp and their water bottles filled. You know, of course, that every soldier, not only Roman ones, carries his own water bottle, because when you are a soldier and fight in different places you never can tell when you might come to a place where there isn't any water, and if in all the bother of getting ready you have forgotten to fill your bottle you might die of thirst. Anyway your Officer would be very angry because of the bother you'd be. So Longinus went round feeling the edges of the spears and looking in the water bottles and he quite forgot about the prisoner.

In the afternoon, after dinner, he remembered again, and he thought he would just go up and see what the four soldiers were doing. So he went up to a little hill outside the town where the three crosses were. There were the soldiers, sitting on the ground and quarrelling over the clothes they had taken from the prisoners.

Each of the crosses had a piece of paper pinned on it with the prisoner's name, so people would know who they were, and also the name of the place they lived in, and why they were being crucified. On the first one was written : " Dysmas, of Bethsaida, a thief." On the third one was written : " Gestas, of Gadara, a thief." And on the middle one was written : " Jesus, of Nazareth, King of the Jews." (Because, you remember, people said that this prisoner pretended to be a king More Important than Cæsar, which was an Imprisoning Thing.) As Longinus came nearer he heard Gestas shouting and cursing Jesus : Dysmas was quite quiet and was just looking at Him all the time.

When they saw Longinus coming the soldiers stopped quarrelling and stood up and saluted. As he was taking the salute, Longinus' prisoner cried out in a very loud voice : " Father, into Thy Hands I commend my spirit," and then he died. Longinus was very surprised, because what the prisoner *meant* was that he was giving his own soul back to God and so was choosing when to die ! You see, any ordinary person would have died long ago, and they had done their best to kill him, but he didn't die until he wanted to.

(If somebody shot you in the Heart, you couldn't say, "I won't die until twenty minutes after I've been shot," could you ?   But God could, if *He* wanted to.)

Suddenly Longinus had a Wonderful Idea. " That was the Son of God ! '' he said, " and I helped to crucify Him. But I didn't know, then. *I* thought He was a traitor, like everybody said He was." *Poor* Longinus ! He was so sorry that he couldn't bear it, and he was just going to tell everybody else that it was God's Son and not a traitor, when suddenly it got very dark, and a great strong wind blew and a thunderstorm began.   All the people who had been looking at the prisoners on their crosses and reading their labels began to go home.   The thunder got louder and louder, and the wind howled and whistled, and the trees began to be struck by lightning and were blown down.   The people were very frightened and they ran and ran, but some were killed by the trees crashing down, and some were struck by the lightning and some were swallowed up with their houses in a great Earthquake.   It was quite the worst and most Frightening Thing that had happened to anybody, ever.

Longinus and his soldiers were very frightened too, but they had to stay in their places because soldiers aren't allowed to run away, however frightened they are.   So they stood close together and waited by the three crosses.   There were two other people there : one was the Mother of Jesus, and the other was his friend called John.

Longinus wanted to ask them about his prisoner being the Son of God, but he didn't want the soldiers to listen, so he didn't.

As soon as the storm died down Longinus marched his men back to the barracks and told them to hurry up and get their things ready and their water bottles filled, because the others had nearly finished theirs. He was very glad he had finished his own things because he *couldn't* stop thinking about Jesus being God and not a traitor, and he was so dreadfully sorry that he had been so horrible to Him. He wished Jesus wasn't dead and that he could *tell* Him how sorry he was. " But it is no good now," he thought.

By the evening everyone was Ready for the Battle. The soldiers were very excited because it was their turn to fight. They kept guessing who would kill the most enemies and who would take the most prisoners. They were very stiff and proud because they nearly always won battles.

Just before their supper, a messenger came to the door of the big Hall and said in a loud voice : " Is Longinus here ? " He had to say it twice more because of the noise the soldiers were making with their shields and things.

" Yes, here I am," said Longinus, and he put down a helmet he had been looking at and went to the door.

" Oh, there you are," said the messenger. " Well, the Governor wants to see you at once."

" All right," said Longinus, " tell him I am coming now."

When he got to the Governor's room, the Governor

said, " Good evening, Longinus." " Good evening,
sir," said Longinus.

" Do you remember the prisoner you fetched last
night ? " said the Governor.

" Oh, yes," said Longinus, " what about him ? I
saw him when he died." But he didn't say anything
about him being God, or that that was why there
was a storm.

" Well," said the Governor, " I heard that he was
dead and as he was *your* prisoner I want you to go and
make sure that he *is* dead. To-morrow is Sunday
and we aren't allowed to have executions on Sundays,
so you must kill him if he is still alive. You had
better spear him, even if you think he *is* dead, so as
to make *quite* sure."

So Longinus took four other men (because it
wouldn't be fair to keep on taking the same four
soldiers when he went out to do Interesting Things),
and they started off again. On their way they could
see the three crosses standing up on the little hill
outside the town. When they got there they went to
the first cross, with Dysmas on it. He was still alive,
so one of the soldiers broke his legs and he died.
At the third cross, with Gestas on it, they found that
he wasn't dead yet either, so another soldier broke
his legs and so he died. When they came to the
middle cross with Longinus' prisoner Jesus on it
Longinus wouldn't let them touch Him. But as the
Governor had ordered him to make *sure* He was dead,
and soldiers *must* obey orders, he drove his spear into
Jesus' side, and as he pulled it out again water and
blood ran out. Longinus turned to go back, feeling

very sad. His eyes hurt him and he rubbed them gently. At once they stopped hurting and he looked up and found that he could easily see far-away things, and nothing looked faint or misty, like it always had before. He looked at the hand he had rubbed them with and found that it was stained with blood off his spear.

As soon as he had marched the four men back to the barracks he went to see his Superior Officer.

"What do you want? I am busy," said the Superior Officer.

"Would you mind very much if I didn't go to the Battle to-morrow?" said Longinus, "I want to go and see a man about some Very Important Business, and I think I shall have to stop being a Centurion."

The Superior Officer was very sorry to hear this, because of Longinus being such a good Centurion, but he said that another Centurion could go instead. "Thank you," said Longinus, "the men are all ready."

"Good," said the Superior Officer, and Longinus went away.

He went straight to the Prisoner's mother, called Mary, whom he had seen by the cross in the storm, and told her all about everything, and how sorry he was.

"Never mind," said Mary, "He knows all about it and He quite understands. But He wants you to stop being a Centurion now and be a Christian, and tell other people about Him being God's Son."

"I *thought* that might happen, I told the Superior Officer so," said Longinus. "Where *is* Our Lord now?"

" I expect you'll see Him one of these days," said Mary.

" Oh," said Longinus, and he went to a place called Cesarea to tell people about Jesus being God and not a traitor. And heaps of people turned into Christians because of what he told them.

One day some Roman soldiers were in Cesarea with another Centurion.

" Look ! There's Longinus ! " they said. " Let's Take him Prisoner because he's a Christian ! " So they did, and they took him to the Roman Governor of Cesarea, who was blind.

" I will let you go again if you say that this statue is God and that Jesus isn't," said the Governor, and he showed Longinus an idol, which was a statue of someone called Phœbus.

"But a *statue* can't be God," said Longinus. "Besides, Jesus *is* God, so I can't say that."

"Well," said the blind Governor, "unless you do, I'll tell the soldiers to cut off your head."

"I can't help that," said Longinus, "that statue *isn't* God and Jesus *is*. He was my prisoner once, so I ought to know. But to prove I am right and you are wrong, as soon as my head is cut off you won't be blind any more."

So the Governor sent for the soldiers and told them to cut off Longinus' head. And as soon as they did, he stopped being blind! He was so surprised that he was wrong about the statue that he became a Christian too, which was a very Good Thing.

Longinus' Special Day is the 15th of March. I wonder if anyone is called after him?

ST. CHRISTOPHER

ONCE upon a time there was a Giant. He was twice as high and twice as wide as the biggest man you have ever seen. He was very, very strong, and could do much harder work than anyone else because of being so big, but he only lived in an ordinary-sized house, so he wasn't very happy because he had to stoop all the time so as not to bump his head. The one proper-sized thing he had was an Enormous Chair. It took up a lot of room in the Dining-room, but the Giant did not mind that because he liked sitting in it so much.

One day, he was sitting in his house on the Enormous Chair and he thought this thought :

" I wish I were a King ! I am so very Big and Strong that I could win *all* the Battles with *all* the other Kings. And I would be the most Special and Important of them all, because I am so Big."

Then he thought another thought, and this was the Other Thought :

" If I can't be a King myself, I shall go and do Strong Things for the Most Special and Important King There Is, and that will be nearly as good."

So he got up out of the Enormous Chair, and he pulled up a young May tree for a walking stick, and he cut off its roots and branches, and started out to find the Most Special and Important King There Is.

He asked everybody he met :

"Which is the Top King? The one who isn't Afraid of Anything?"

And everybody said that King Mundus was.

So the Giant went and worked for King Mundus, who had a Palace made of Silver, with china floors, and Gold doors and furniture, and Purple Velvet Curtains. The King and all his Courtiers dressed in Fine Raiment, and the King had a Diamond Walking Stick.

There was an Enormous Army at the Palace, but it never fought anyone because King Mundus was the Top King, so he didn't need Battles. But he used the Army to help him to go hunting for Elephants, but he never killed them; he kept them to ride on afterwards. Really, King Mundus was the Bravest King that the Giant had ever seen. Even when Lions Sprang Out at him when he was out hunting Elephants, he just used to hit them with his Diamond Walking Stick, and they fell down dead.

One day they were riding along in a Procession with the Giant and the King all Stiff and Proud in front; and some of the soldiers were singing behind them. In the song was something about Satan, and every time the soldiers sang the word "Satan" King Mundus turned Rather Pale.

"Why do you turn Rather Pale when they sing 'Satan'?" asked the Giant, "I thought you said *you* were the Top King, and so you oughtn't to be frightened of anything at all."

"But King Satan is more Top than all the Kings, even me," said King Mundus.

"Well," said the Giant, "why didn't you tell me

that before? I said that I wanted to work for the Most Special and Important King there is, and you aren't if you're frightened of Satan. Good-bye."

So the Giant went off to find King Satan. He didn't have to go very far because, coming to meet him, he saw another Procession. Riding at the head of it, and rather a long way in front, was a very Proud and Grand King. He had a black horse and he was dressed all in Black Velvet except for his Silver Crown, and he was so Haughty and Stiff that even the great big Giant felt Rather Frightened, but not *very*.

"What do you want, and why are you here?" said this Grand Person.

"I am a Giant, and I am looking for King Satan, so that I can work for him, because he is more Important than the Top King."

"Well, I am King Satan," said the Grand Person, "you needn't do very hard work. Just ride along beside me and look Stiff and Proud."

So the Giant turned round and rode beside King Satan, and after them followed the Procession of Soldiers, and Judges, and Sailors, and Workmen, and Kings and Queens with crowns on, and all sorts of Elegant People, all galloping their horses to try and keep up with King Satan and the Giant.

They hadn't gone very far when they came to a Church with a Crucifix outside it.

"I don't think we'll go past here, I don't much like Crucifixes," said King Satan.

The Giant thought this was Rather Funny, but he didn't say anything, and they all turned round and went another way. Soon they came to another

Church with another Crucifix, and the same thing happened.

" Are you *frightened* of a wooden Cross ? " said the Giant. " If not, *why* don't you like going near one ? What are they for, and who is the man on them ? " (Because the Giant was not a Christian, and he had never heard of Our Lord.)

"Well, yes, I am afraid," said King Satan, " because the man is Christ the King, Who is stronger than I. But never mind all that, come along with me, and I will make you Very Grand."

" Well, I can't go with you if you are not the *Very* Top King," said the Giant, " I *must* go and work for King Christ. Good-bye."

So the Giant went away to look for Christ the King, Who was stronger than King Satan, who was stronger than King Mundus, who said he was the Top King.

One day he found a Wise Old Man who lived all alone in a little Hut in a Dark Forest near a Deep River without a bridge.

" Do you know where I can find Christ the King ? " the Giant asked him. " You see, I want to work for him because he is stronger than King Satan, who is stronger than King Mundus, who is the Top King."

" You can only work for him if you fast and pray as well," said the Wise Old Man.

" Well, *I* can't," said the Giant, " because if I fast I won't be so strong, and I don't know how to pray."

" Well, there *is* another way," said the Wise Old Man. " Do you see that Deep River ? Nobody seems to be able to cross it without falling in. Now, you go and live beside it and Carry people Over, because you are so Strong. It won't be too deep for you, will it ? "

" Of *course* it won't be too deep for me," said the Giant, " but I want to work for Christ the King, I don't want to go carrying a lot of silly people over the River all the time. Why can't they have a bridge ? "

" Because the river runs so fast that it washes the bridge away every time," said the Wise Old Man. " Besides, you *will* be working for Christ the King, because He *specially* told me what He wanted you to do. But you won't be allowed to see Him until later ; no one ever is."

So the Giant built himself a house on the bank of the Deep River, and whenever anyone wanted to go across, they used to ring a Clanging Bell that hung on a tree that was just outside, and the Giant would come out and say :

" Do you want to cross the River ? "

And they would say :

" Yes, please."

And the Giant would say :

" Well, jump up ! " and they would jump up on his back and he would carry them over. But if they were too old and couldn't jump up, he would lift them.

One night, right in the middle of the Night, the Bell rang : " Clang ! Clang ! Clang ! " And before the Giant had time to get out of bed and put on his dressing-gown and bedroom-slippers, a voice said :

" Carrier ! Will you carry me across the River ? "

But when he got outside there was no one there !

The Giant thought this was very funny and he went back to bed.

"It must have been a Dream," he thought.

As soon as he had gone to sleep again the Bell rang : "Clang ! Clang ! Clang ! " And before the Giant had time to put on his dressing-gown and bedroom-slippers a voice said :

"Carrier ! Will you carry me across the River?"

But when he got outside there was no one there *again!* The Giant thought that this was *very* funny and he went back to bed again. " That must have been a dream, too," he said to himself.

As soon as he had gone to sleep again the Bell rang : " Clang ! Clang ! Clang ! " And before he had time to get out of bed and put on his dressing-gown and bedroom-slippers a voice said :

"Carrier ! Will you carry me across the River?"

When he got outside there stood a little boy.

"Hullo !" said the Giant. "Was it you the other times ? " But the little boy only said :

" Are you *sure* you can carry me ? "

The Giant laughed because it was such a *very* little boy, and he was such a *very* big Giant.

" Of course I can ! " he said, and he lifted the little boy right up on to his shoulder, because he was so small and light. Then he took his great walking-stick, made of a May tree, in his hand and stepped down into the Deep River. Suddenly the wind began to blow and the water got deeper and deeper, and it flowed so fast that it nearly knocked the Giant over.

" Are you sure you can carry me ? " asked the little boy.

" Of *course* I can ! " said the Giant, and the stones at the bottom of the River began to roll along, and they nearly tripped him up. The little boy felt heavier than he looked, and it was certainly difficult to walk.

" Are you *still* sure you can carry me ? " asked the little boy.

" Of *course* I am sure ! " said the Giant Rather

Crossly. He wished the little boy wouldn't keep *on* asking him ; it interrupted him when he was trying not to fall down. He thought that the little boy was afraid of being dropped, but he didn't look a bit frightened. It rained so hard in the poor Giant's face that he could scarcely see, and the little boy got heavier and heavier, and the Giant's shoulders ached and ached.

" *Now* are you sure ? " said the little boy, and the water began to carry the Giant away, it was so Deep and Swift.

" No, but I'll try and manage," said the Giant, and

he tried so hard that, in spite of the wind and rain and thunder and lightning, he at last got to the other side, and then the Storm stopped ! He was so tired and out of breath that he just put down the little boy and lay down on the River Bank and shut his eyes. After a minute he opened them again and said :

" I have *never* carried anything so heavy in all my life ! Who are you ? Why weren't you frightened ? Even *I* was, rather, in that Very Deep part."

" I am Christ the King, Whom you wanted to work for," said the little boy, " I wasn't frightened of the Storm because I made it myself. I was very heavy because everybody gives Me their Troubles to carry, so, of course, you were carrying them as well. Now you really are My servant because you have never worked so hard before, and so I will show you something Special. Stick your walking-stick into the ground."

The Giant did, and what *do* you suppose happened ? Well, you remember how he had cut off all the roots and branches to make it into a stick ? Well, it grew in the ground and made new branches and leaves and flowers all in one single minute ! The Giant saw it do it.

When he turned round to ask Christ the King (Who had been pretending to be a little boy so that the Giant wouldn't know him) about it, he had gone away !

After that the Giant was always called Christopher, which means Christ-Carrier, because he had carried Christ the King.

Have you ever noticed that in a lot of motor-cars,

near the driver's seat, there is a little blue and silver picture ? Sometimes it is all silver. Well, if you look at one closely next time you see one, you will see that it is Christopher carrying Christ-the-King-pretending-to-be-a-little-boy. We put the picture on our cars because Christopher still looks after us in Traffic or on journeys like he used to look after the travellers by the Deep River. So now he is the Special Saint for Travellers, and his Special Day is July the 25th. Now I expect you have noticed that there ought to be Two Special Days in this story, but I will tell you when the other one is in case you haven't. It is the Last Sunday in October, and it belongs to Christ the King.

ST. NICHOLAS

ONCE upon a time there was a Bishop, and his name was Nicholas, and he lived Seventeen Hundred years ago, which is a long time.

Well, one year, there was a Famine. (A Famine is when there is absolutely Nothing Left to Eat Anywhere, and so people have to eat Grass and roots of trees boiled into Soup, and things like that.) Well, in this Famine, Nicholas was travelling over some mountains to look for some food for his people, when he came to a Small Hotel, all by itself in between two mountains. It was nearly Night by then, and he thought he had better sleep there, and go on in the morning. He was very hungry and he would have loved to have had some Supper, but he knew that there would not be any because of the Famine.

But when he was settled by the fire in the Hotel, the Hotel Man came in and started laying the table !

" Are you going to give me some Supper ? " asked Nicholas.

The Hotel Man laughed and said that he had a Secret Store of food down in his Deepest Darkest Cellar, and that Nicholas could have some, if he liked. Nicholas was very pleased, he *was* so hungry ! He hadn't had anything to eat, except some Dock Leaves and Sorrel, since the day before yesterday breakfast time.

Soon the Hotel Man brought in a dish with a silver dish cover over it and put it in front of Nicholas' place.   Then he gave him a square green plate, with white edges, to eat off.

"Help yourself!" he said, and he lifted off the dish cover.   Inside was some very nice-looking Salted Meat (like ham is) with Dumplings round the edge.

"I am sorry I can't give you any potatoes," said

the Hotel Man, "but there aren't any left, because of the Famine."

"Never mind, I like dumplings," said Nicholas, and he looked at the supper again.   Then he smelt it.   Then he looked at the Hotel Man, who was humming a little tune and pretending not to notice.

"Where did you get this meat?   There isn't any left in the whole land," asked Nicholas.

" Oh, it's just some I had in a Secret Store in the Cellar," said the Hotel Man, and he flipped the table with the dinner napkin which he kept hanging over his arm.

" Is this all there is, or is there some more ? " said Nicholas.

" There is a little left in a tub in the cellar," said the Hotel Man. " Haven't you got enough there ? Shall I go and get you some more ? " And he picked up the dish.

" No, leave the dish, and show me where you got it from," said Nicholas.

" I'd rather you didn't go all the way down there," said the Hotel Man, " I'll bring it up."

" Take me down *at once!* " said Nicholas, very Loud and Fierce, and the Hotel Man said, " All *right!* I am not deaf," in rather a frightened voice.

So they went down and down the very steep steps into the Deepest Darkest Cellar. There stood the Tub ! It was painted green and it had Iron Rings round it. It had a wooden lid.

" Bring me a light, please, I want to see in it ! " said Nicholas.

The Hotel Man brought a candle, in a blue candle-stick, and Nicholas lifted up the lid and looked inside. It was half-full of Salted Meat, just the same as the meat upstairs. Then he blessed it (like he could because he was a Bishop), and what *do* you suppose happened ? It really was the Most Surprising Thing that the Hotel Man had ever seen ! Out jumped three little boys ! The wicked Hotel Man hadn't got any more meat for his customers, so he had killed

the little boys and Pickled them and Peppered them and cut them into little Squares and popped them into his Salt meat tub.

Nicholas took them away with him and gave them back to their mother, who had been looking for them everywhere. When they told her what had happened, of course she told all her friends, so everybody said that Nicholas was the Special Saint for Children, because of the little boys. His Special Day is the 6th of December, near Christmas, and if you say " St. Nicholas, St. Nicholas, St. Nicholas," very quickly and very often, you will see that it turns into " Santa Claus," and they are both the same person ! And Santa Claus is Special for Children, too.

ST. BRIGID OF IRELAND

Now *this* Story can be for Scotch *or* Irish people, and there is only one difference—If you are Scotch you pretend that there isn't a G in the middle and call her Bride, and if you are Irish you pretend that the D at the end is a T and call her Bridget.

Well, one day Brigid, who was living in Ireland, thought she would like to go across to Iona and see how her friend Columba was getting on. (Columba was telling all the Scotch People about being Christians and Brigid was telling the Irish People.)

So she went down to the Sea and she asked a Fisherman could she Borrow his Boat so that she could go across to see Colum-cille (Columba was often called Colum-cille, which means "Columba of the Church," because he was born in a little house which was close up against a Church).

"Well," said the Fisher-man, "I would like to lend you my Boat but I am afraid I am So Busy that I can't Spare the Time to come and sail it for you."

"I can sail it myself, then," said Brigid.

"But a lady can't go All Across the Sea in a Boat Alone!" said the Fisher-man. "You must have a Gillie, Brigid, you really *must*. What would we all do, at all, if you were drowned or lost on the way?"

(A Gillie is a Boy, or sometimes a servant or sometimes a son.)

"I have some Gillies of my own who know the

way," said Brigid, " and thank you very much for lending me your Boat."

So the Fisher-man put up the sail and Brigid got in, and the Fisher-man pushed the Boat out.   And as he pushed he thought to himself :

" Well, *I* can't see any Gillies ! "

Just then Brigid said :

" Come, Gillies !   I am ready now ! "

And there came flying round Hundreds of little Birds called Oyster-catchers with red legs and black and white feathers.   And some of them flew behind the Boat to make a Wind for the Sail, and some flew in front of it to show the way, and away sailed Brigid to see how her friend Columba was getting along in Iona !

When she got there, after she and Colum-cille had been chatting for a bit, she said :

" What shall we do for all my little Gillies that brought me here so safely ? "

" Let's ask St. Michael," said Columba, " because he looks after all the Sea and Islands."

So they did, and St. Michael Rather Wanted to make them All White instead of Black and White, but Brigid said :

" Oh ! *please* no ! I *love* them being black and white with their dear little red legs. Do let them stay like they are, only let the white part be like a Cross, so that when they fly, people will remember Our Lord."

So that now, if you look at an Oyster-catcher, when he is flying over your head, you will see that his White Part is shaped like a Cross. And in Scotland they are still called Bride's Gillies.

St. Brigid's Special Day is on February 1st, and I know that Hundreds of People are called after her because she was so Nice.

ST. COLUMBA

THIS is a Story for People who live in Scotland, but especially those who live on the West Side of Scotland, so you know who it will be about, don't you? (Well, yes, it *could* be about St. Brigid, I know, but she *really* belongs to Ireland now.) Well? Who? St. Columba, of course! Or Colum-cille as he is often called.

I am not going to tell you about how he was the first person to tell the people in Scotland about being Christians, because you know that. Or about how he chose the little island called Iona to build a Monastery for monks there, because you know that, too. But this is about when Columba was living on Iona with his monks, and the Fame of him was soon over the water to all the other Islands, and Everybody wanted to see him, he was so Kind and so Different.

One day, a little Boy called Ailein was sitting on a skerry on the Island of Rhum and was looking at the Boats going out. (They were the little round boats made of wicker and covered with skins, called Coracles.) And the little Boy thought this thought:

" If only I could get across to Iona to see Columcille, perhaps he might bless me. But I haven't a Coracle."

Just as he was thinking, there came a Gentleman who said :

" What would you give to a man, Ailein, who would sail you across to Iona and back ? "

" I would be his Gillie for ever and ever," said Ailein. (In case People who Don't Live in Scotland don't know what a Gillie is, he is sometimes a son and sometimes a servant, like we say Boy.)

He had only just said it when there they were

in a Coracle, sailing so fast to Iona that the Wind could hardly keep up with them to keep the sails full !

When they had landed on Iona the Gentleman said :

" Now hurry up and see Columba, and I will wait for you."

Ailein ran up the Beach and soon found an Old and Beautiful Man who Looked like a King, and who Dressed like a Monk. He was mending the broken wing of a Sea Gull, and the Sea Gull wasn't minding it a bit.

" Well, Ailein," said the old man, " so you managed to come after all ! Kneel down, and I will Bless

you. Then I will Tell you Something and Give you
Something."

So Ailein knelt down and Colum-cille blessed him.

"Now," he said, going on with the Sea Gull's
wing, "I'll Tell you something about the Gentleman
who brought you here." And he told him something.

"Now, I'll Give you something." And he gave
him a Candle.

Ailein ran back to the Gentleman and they sailed
back to Rhum.

"Praise be to the Good Being!" said Ailein (that
was his name for God). "Now I have seen Colum-
cille and had his Blessing."

"Yes," said the Gentleman, "and now you must
remember your Promise, and be my Gillie for Ever
and Ever."

And, as he was speaking, Ailein saw that it was
really Satan pretending to be a Gentleman! But he
wasn't a bit frightened because of what Columba had
told him.

He pulled out his Candle that had been Blessed
by Columba, and he lit it and he said:

"Please, Gentleman, before I am your Gillie, may
I be the Gillie of Jesus, like Colum-cille, just until
my Candle burns out?"

"No, it is too long," said Satan.

Ailein lit the other end too, and, holding it side-
ways so that it wouldn't go out, he said:

"Until it burns out now?"

"Yes, it is not a very Important Thing to want.
You can be Jesus' Gillie until the Candle is burnt out."

Then Ailein blew out the Candle and said :

" Please, Gentleman, it will never *burn* out as long as I live, because I will never light it again, and *you can't!* " And he popped it into a bowl of Holy Water, which, as you know, the Devil can't touch !

" *Well!* " said Satan as he went away, " I must say, that what with Columba and Ailein, Jesus does have Gillies with Good Ideas."

After that, Ailein was often called Gilliosa, which means Jesus' Gillie, and he went and lived with Columba (whose Good Idea it was about the Candle) for the rest of his life.

St. Columba's Special Day is on June 9th, but very few People that aren't Scotch are called after him. (And I'll tell you another thing, because this Story has such a lot about Gillies in it, and that is that most names that begin with Gill-something mean Servant- or Son- of someone. Like Gilchrist, Servant of Christ ; or Gillespie, Servant of the Bishop ; or Gillander, Son of Andrew. So perhaps someone will be called by one of these names instead of Columba, and, if they are, then they can have this Story for their Special one.)

ST. FRANCIS OF ASSISI

ONCE upon a time, in a very old town in Italy called Assisi, there lived a Silk Merchant whose name was Pietro Bernadone. (Pietro is the Italian for Peter.) Well, this Silk Merchant used to spend most of his time in France buying silks to make dresses for the rich ladies in Italy. So, because he was there such a lot and he made his money there, he loved France.

One day, when he went home with his silks to Assisi, he found that his wife had got a son for him, called Giovanni (which is the Italian for John). Pietro wasn't very pleased about this because he didn't like the name Giovanni, but he thought that it would be a good thing to have a son who could go and buy silk for him in France when he grew up, so he changed the baby's name to Francis and felt much happier because he had made up a new name.

When Francis was older and went to school, his favourite things to do were Fighting and Learning French. None of the others learned French, so he felt very grand. He was very good at fighting, but he was never very tall, so it was rather difficult. Even when he was Grown Up he was a small man with dark hair and bright brown eyes and a sunburnt face. While he was still a little boy he loved stories of Battles and Sieges and Martyrs and Heroes, and he decided that he would do all these things when he was a man. So, when he was Twenty he went with a lot of his friends, on horses, to fight with the next town called Perugia. No one thought very much of Perugia, so Francis and his friends did not bother to take very many swords and things. And instead of putting on armour and swords and shields and helmets they put on their very Best and Brightest-coloured clothes. Francis' clothes were the Brightest and Best of all, because of his Father being a Silk Merchant, and he had on a Red Velvet Cloak with a Silver Collar and Fastens, and he had a Shiny Black Horse with Red and Silver Harness. Well, when they got near to Perugia they weren't really being a bit careful and were telling each other funny stories and playing guessing games instead of Keeping a Look Out. So of course the people of Perugia saw them coming from miles away because of their Bright-coloured Clothes, and they rushed out and took them all Prisoners before they had time to think ! They kept all the horses and swords for their own soldiers and put Francis and his friends in Prison for a whole Year.

They were all very sad at being in Prison and having to keep the same clothes on all the time, and they said it was all Francis' fault for starting it. But Francis kept cheering them up and making them laugh, and he made up funny bits of poetry about them all, so they weren't so unhappy after all.

When they had been in Prison for 364 days (how many days in a year ?) Francis had a Dream, and the Dream was—He saw Our Lord standing with piles of swords and silks and cloaks all round Him and every

sword had a handle like a Cross. While Francis
was wondering what it was all for, Our Lord said :

"These are the things that I give to the people who
work for Me, and these are the swords that I give to
them so that they can fight for Me."

When he woke up in the morning Francis knew
that Our Lord didn't want him to have Bright Clothes
any more while he was here, but that he must wait
until he got to Heaven and he could have them then
if he wanted them. Also that he mustn't fight with
the Perugians or anyone at all any more but only the
Devil, whose name is Satan. Francis felt very sad
about this, because he *did* love fighting, especially
with Bright-coloured Clothes on and with beautiful
Red and Silver Reins for his horse. While he was
thinking about the Dream, Satan came up behind
him, very quietly so that he wouldn't hear, and put
an Idea into his head quickly and went away before
anyone saw him. And this was the Idea :

"If I do not dress in my satin and velvet clothes
and fight people, all my friends who like doing that
too will not be friends with me any more. So I
don't think I'll do what Our Lord said, it will be so
dull with no friends and no fighting."

The next day (that was 365 days) Francis and all
his friends were let out of Prison, because it was the
end of the year, and they all started home for Assisi.
The Perugians wouldn't give them back their horses,
so they had to walk. It took them a very long time ;
nearly all day. As he was walking along the road
and thinking how nice it would be when he got home
and could put on his Blue and Gold Cloak after having

worn his Red and Silver one for a whole year, Francis
saw a very poor old Raggy Man coming along to
meet him.

" I *am* so cold ! " said the man.   " *I* used to have
a fine red and silver cloak like yours, but I lost it.
Now I am so poor I can't buy another one."

Now, although Francis did not know it, there were
two people watching him, to see what he would do.

One was Our Lord, Who was standing behind an
Oak Tree quite close to the Raggy Man, and He said
to Himself :

" If Francis gives his Red and Silver Cloak to that
Raggy Man it means that he is going to listen to that
Dream that I sent him and that he is going to be on
My side."   The other person who was watching was
Satan, and he was hiding behind a Gorse Bush and

hoping that Francis would not see him, because he was so close. He had on a Red and Silver Cloak just like Francis' and he said to himself :

" If Francis *doesn't* give his Red and Silver Cloak to that Raggy Man it means that he is going to listen to that Idea I put in his head and that he is going to be on *my* side."

Francis thought : " I'll give him my cloak, if he really *has* lost his—no, I won't, because people will laugh at me if I go home without one—yes, I will, because I don't really need it, I've got the Blue and Gold one." So he said to the Raggy Man :

" Here you are, change clothes with me, mine are warmer than yours, and I am not a bit cold. And if I have the Raggy ones I can pretend to be you and give the people at home a Surprise."

So they both laughed and changed clothes and Francis went on to Assisi. Satan was so cross that his side hadn't won that he *stamped* on the ground behind the Gorse Bush and hurt his foot on a stone. Then he started to run along behind the hedge after Francis to see what he would do next, but he kept tripping over the Red and Silver Cloak, so he went home, muttering to himself. But Our Lord walked along beside Francis for a minute and said :

" Never mind if your friends won't talk to you if you are Raggy, you can be a friend of Mine, if you like, and that will be much more Special and Important."

So after that Francis always had on plain grey or brown clothes with a leather belt.

One day there was a poor old woman with a heavy

bundle of vegetables that kept *on* coming undone. First a turnip rolled out ; and then, when she was stooping to pick it up, out fell a beetroot ; then four potatoes ; then a carrot and three cauliflowers ! Then she dropped the whole bundle all over the road and sat in the middle of everything and began to cry ! So Francis cheered her up and did up the bundle and gave her his leather belt to keep it all together. After that he always had a piece of rope instead of a belt, because it was more useful and much cheaper.

Now as soon as it was settled that Francis was going to be on Our Lord's side against Satan, lots of very Interesting and Exciting Things happened to him, and one of them was about a Wolf.

One day as he was walking along in his brown clothes and a rope for a belt he came to some workmen mending the road. So he thought he would stop for a minute and tell them about being very Poor here so as to be very Rich in Heaven.

" Because," he said, " if you were very Rich here it might make you Proud and Haughty, but you can't be Proud and Haughty in Heaven ; nobody is, so it is much better to be Rich there. Besides, Heaven lasts so much longer."

But the workmen thought that it was such a long time to wait until they got to Heaven that they'd rather be Rich *now*. And Francis said :

" That is exactly like eating the Sugar on your Birthday Cake *first*, because then you have to eat *all* the Cake and there will be no Sugar at the end. If you eat the Cake first you can be as long as you like eating the Sugar, and you needn't have anything else to Spoil the Taste."

But the workmen thought that Francis was silly to try and make them be Poor when they were trying to be as Rich as they could.

Well now, about the Wolf. When he left the workmen Francis came to a town called Gubbio, where all the people were Misers! And he wanted to tell them about the Good Idea of being Poor. But there was no one there to listen! Francis thought that this was very funny, so he knocked at somebody's door and said :

" Where are all the people ? I want to tell them something."

The lady who opened the door said :

" Oh! didn't you know? Nobody goes out of their houses unless heaps of us go together, because of the Wolf."

" What Wolf ? " asked Francis.

" There's a Wolf who lives at the end of the Town," said the lady, whose name was Rina, " and every single day he eats somebody. He is the very Worst Kind of Wolf, because you never hear him coming, and suddenly he *Pounces* on you ! You'd better mind out."

" How very Tiresome," said Francis, " I *am* sorry for you. I think perhaps I'd better go and speak to it and then perhaps it won't."

" No, don't," said Rina, " he'll only eat you, and that won't be any help at all."

But Francis started off in his Brown Clothes and his Rope and all the people looked out of their windows

to see what he was going to do. He had just got to
the End of the Town when suddenly the Worst Wolf
he had ever seen Sprang out at him ! Its mouth was
open and its Red Tongue was hanging out, and its
Paws were all ready to Knock him Over, and (Rina
was quite right) it was Enormous !

Francis said :

" Wait ! " in a very loud and sudden voice and the
Wolf was so surprised that it stopped right in the
middle of its Spring. No one had ever said " Wait ! "
to him so suddenly ; he didn't like it ; it made him
jump. Usually people tried to run away. Then
Francis quickly made the Sign of the Cross and
blessed the Wolf. This surprised him more than
ever ; no one had ever blessed him before and he
liked it. He shut his mouth and wagged his tail and
waited to see what Francis would do next.

" Brother Wolf," said Francis (the Wolf liked that
too, no one had ever called him Brother before),
" *Why* do you eat all these people ? Don't you *know*
that they're so frightened that they daren't come out
of their houses ? And you've killed all their sheep
and cows and things so that they're nearly starving."

" I know," said the Wolf, " I don't much *like* eating
them ; they're too thin ; but there *isn't* anything
else to eat, and I must eat *something*, I can't starve to
death, can I ? "

" Well, no," said Francis, " you can't. But perhaps you didn't know how Perfectly Abominable you
are ? You are the Very Worst Wolf I ever saw. If *I*
promise *you* that you will always have enough to eat,
will *you* promise *me* that you'll never eat People again ? "

The Wolf wagged his tail and promised. Francis held out his hand and the Wolf put his paw into it and they Sealed the Bargain.

" Come back to the Town with me," said Francis, " and you'll see what I am going to do."

So the Wolf licked Francis' hand and trotted along beside him into the Town. As soon as they saw them coming, the people all ran into their houses and shut their doors, because of the Wolf.

" Come out ! " said Francis, " I want to tell you something."

So the people all came out again and Francis said :

" Will you promise me to feed Brother Wolf, always, if he promises never to eat anyone again ? " And the People all promised and said, " Yes, we will." So Francis said :

" Well, I'll put you and Brother Wolf On Your Honours."

Then the Wolf held out his paw, and he and Francis shook hands again and all the people cheered.

If you want to know what happened to the Wolf after Francis had gone, he used to be like everybody's Dog, and he barked at tramps. But he got rather Fat because he had such a lot to eat.

When Francis went away from Gubbio, some of the young men who lived there went with him. They gave all their things to the very poor people and dressed like Francis did because of his Good Idea of being Poor. Some of them went to some towns and some of them went to others, so that they could tell everybody about the Good Idea.

Well, one day Francis and one of his friends called

Antony were going to a town called Rimini. (Antony's home was in a place called Padua, like Francis' was Assisi, and he was the same St. Antony who finds things for you when you have lost them.) But the people in Rimini wouldn't listen to them. They all went away and talked about something else, very loud, so that they could not hear what Francis was saying. So he and Antony went down to the sea-shore (Rimini was at the sea-side), and Francis said :

" Come out, Fish ! I want to tell you something ! "

And all the fish came and stood on their tails in the water, with their heads sticking out. The little fish were in front in the shallow water, and the middle-sized fish were in the middle in the middling-deep water, and the big fish were at the back in the deepest water, and there were even some Sharks and a Whale at the *very* back. And Francis told them how lucky they were always to have something ready for them to eat. And they could even choose what coloured water they would live in : some blue ; some grey ; some green ; and some brown like Francis' clothes. And they could live in Rivers if they did not like the Sea being salty, or Lakes ; or Ponds. And he told them that it was God Who made it all nice and ready for them. The Fish were very pleased to hear this because they never knew who had made it nice and ready, and they had always wanted to know. Then Francis told them some Important Things about what Fish had done. Like the Haddock who brought a penny to Our Lord when He hadn't got one to pay His Taxes with.

And now *all* Haddocks have a mark of a Finger and Thumb on their shoulders where St. Peter picked up the one that brought the penny.

While Francis was talking, all the People of Rimini (who wouldn't listen before) came up behind him to listen now, because they had never seen such an Exciting Thing as those Fish standing up in the water. And they were sorry they had been so rude to Francis when he had done such Exciting Things.

Another day, when Francis was walking along the road with some of his friends, all dressed in their brown clothes and their ropes in case anyone's bundle came undone, they saw a flock of Starlings all twittering in a hedge. So Francis said to the Starlings :

" Stop twittering a minute, Birds ! I want to tell you something ! "

So they stopped and he told them (like the Fishes) how lucky *they* were to have everything ready for *them*, like Trees and Berries and Worms. And all sorts of other birds came and listened, and they sat on the trees and hedges and all over the ground so close together that the Youngest Thrush (the sort that hops about with a very short tail and yellow edges to its beak) hadn't any room, so it came and sat on Francis' head. Francis didn't mind, even though its toes *were* rather Pricky. Then he told them some Important Things that had happened to Birds. Like the Robin (who used to be brown all over) who was so sorry for Our Lord when He was on the Cross that he came and sat so close to Him that he pricked himself on the Crown of Thorns ; and now all Robins have red breasts. And about how the Holy Spirit pretended to be a Dove when He went to Our Lord's Baptism. The Doves liked this story so much that when all the other birds had gone away, they flew beside Francis and his friends all the way back to the house where they all lived together so that they could be as Poor as they liked without Bothering people. So they made nests for the Doves in the Garden, and they stayed there always.

Once Francis was teaching some people at Christmas time about when Our Lord was a Baby, and the people were being very stupid about it and they *couldn't* understand. So he took one of their babies for a minute, and sent a little boy for a big box, and a little girl for some hay. Then he put the hay in the box and the baby on the hay.

"There now!" he said. "Our Lord was like *that*, and Our Lady was kneeling *here*, and St. Joseph was *here*, and the cows and St. Joseph's donkey that Our Lady rode on were *There! Now* do you see?"

And the people did. But afterwards they always had a Crib in their church at Christmas to remind them of what Francis had told them. Then other people thought that Francis' idea was so good that *they* had a Crib, too. Now everybody does, but it was St. Francis who Invented it. He Invented singing Carols, too, because he thought the Little Baby Lord would like them better than hymns.

St. Francis did lots of other Interesting Things that are written in other books. And he made such a lot of friends who liked his Good Idea about being Poor, that now there are Hundreds and Hundreds of them. I expect you have seen Friars (like French for

Brother, like Francis called the wolf) or, anyway, Nuns, dressed in Brown with Ropes round their waists? Sometimes it is Grey, not Brown. Well, they are Franciscans, called after St. Francis, and they are still very Poor.

St. Francis' Special Day is on the 4th of October, and heaps of people are called after him, even some other Saints.

ST. ELIZABETH OF HUNGARY

ONCE upon a time there was a Princess called Elizabeth and she was Four Years Old. She lived in Hungary, but she had to go to another place called Thuringia, because when she grew up she was going to marry Prince Ludwig of Thuringia and be Princess Elizabeth of Thuringia.

Elizabeth was very pleased and excited at going such a long way all by herself, but her Mother, the Queen of Hungary, was sad to lose her only little girl so soon. However, she was very Brave, and she gave Elizabeth some new clothes and new toys and a Velvet Coat, and a Silver Mug with her name on it.

Now Thuringia was more than a Hundred Miles from Hungary and Elizabeth was much too little to ride all the way on horseback like everybody else did, so what do you suppose she went in? A Silver Cradle! It was hung between two horses. One was called Lac (which means Milk) because he was white, and the other was called Mel (which means Honey) because he was pale brown. It was rather like a Hammock, and Elizabeth sat inside. She had Blue Silk pillows and a Red Velvet cover with E for Elizabeth on it, and she had a little Gold crown on her head.

Behind Lac and Mel followed twelve other horses, all carrying things. One carried Elizabeth's Silver

Bath ; another Jewels ; and another Silk and Satin to make her clothes when she got older. Sometimes Lac went a little faster than Mel, and that made the Cradle swing, and Elizabeth loved it !

When they arrived at Thuringia it was Long After Bedtime, and as soon as she had had a quick supper of milk and biscuits she was put to bed. Prince Ludwig's mother, Queen Sophia, slept with her the first night, in case she was frightened, but after that she slept with Princess Agnes, who was Four Years Old, too, and was Prince Ludwig's little sister.

Elizabeth, when she grew older, used to read a lot to herself about Our Lord, and she Loved Him very much, but Queen Sophia and Agnes did not know Him very well.

One day (it was the 15th of August, a day when we all go to Church) the Queen told the two Princesses to put on their Best Rich Dresses and their Crowns and to go to Mass with her. There were other Kings and Queens with crowns on there, and Queen Sophia took Elizabeth and Agnes to the Very Front seat, and sat there all Stiff and Proud between them.

After a little while Elizabeth took off her crown and knelt down. Queen Sophia was so angry that she said quite loud :

"What *are* you doing, Elizabeth ? Kings and Queens don't kneel, they are too Important, and put on your crown at *once* ! "

"I am very sorry," said Elizabeth, " but how can I sit and be Grand and Proud when Our Lord is here, and how can I keep on my Golden Crown when He only has a Crown of Thorns ? He is much more

Important than us because we *are* only People, even if we are Kings and Queens."

Queen Sophia got Very Red, but she didn't say anything, and she kept her crown on and went on being Grand and Proud, because she had forgotten that Our Lord was so *much* more Important than Kings and Queens with Crowns On.

After Elizabeth was grown up she married Queen

Sophia's son, Prince Ludwig, and she loved him and he was very kind to her and gave her a Rosary made of Coral, and a Penknife with E for Elizabeth on it. But Queen Sophia didn't like her because she made her feel Ashamed when she always would take off her crown in Church.

One day Elizabeth had been out to see an old man who was ill in the village. She had taken him two Red Blankets because he had not enough bed-clothes, and some bread and some Honey for his sore Throat, and some Cocoa. He loved cocoa because it

Reminded him of Chocolates. She was just coming back along the road, rather Late for Dinner and wondering what Queen Sophia would say, when she saw a man lying by the hedge. She went and looked at him to see if he was all right, because people who lie beside roads have sometimes been Run Over or something, and then she saw that he had Leprosy very badly. Now Leprosy is a very Catching Illness and Elizabeth might have caught it and given it to her children, so she did not touch him for a minute, while she stood and thought ; and this is what she thought :

" What shall I do ? Because if I give Leprosy to my children it will be a Dreadful Thing, and besides they will give it to everybody else. But I can't Possibly leave this very Ill Man here, because he ought to be in bed. *And*, as he doesn't seem to have a bed of his own, I ought to take him home with me."

In the end she took him home to the Palace, leaning on her arm, and put him to bed in Prince Ludwig's bed because she knew that the servants would be very Angry if she put the raggy old man in one of their beds because of Leprosy being so Catching.

While she was downstairs, seeing about hot water bottles and things, Queen Sophia went into Prince Ludwig's room to put some of his things away, he was rather untidy, and she saw the Ill Man in the bed ! At first she was very frightened, because, of course, she thought he must be a Burglar hiding ; but the man, who was very glad to be so comfily in bed, smiled at her and said :

" Princess Elizabeth said I could be in this bed

because I haven't got a bed of my own, wasn't it
Kind of her ?   She said she was coming back in a
minute."

Queen Sophia was Furiously Angry, because of
Leprosy being so Catching, and she went and called
Prince Ludwig, who was downstairs waiting for dinner,
and she made him come upstairs to see.

"Just *look* what Elizabeth has done now ! " she
cried.   "She has brought a Leper here and has put
him in your Bed ! Do you hear me ? In your
Bed ! "

Prince Ludwig looked down at the poor man.

" It is Our Lord Himself," he said quietly, and the
old man disappeared !

Our Lord sometimes pretends to be someone else
to the people who love Him best, to see if they are
really as kind to other people as they say they would
be. If they Knew it was Our Lord of *course* they
would do anything for Him, but sometimes we can't
be Bothered to do things for Ordinary People even
though He did say that doing things for them was
the same as doing them for Him.

Another very Interesting Thing happened to Elizabeth. It was a very cold winter, and the Village
People's corn had not grown properly in the summer
before, so they had nothing to eat. Now there was a
lot of corn in the Palace Granary, but not enough for
Everybody, so Prince Ludwig said that it was no
use giving it to Only a Few because it would not be
Fair on the Others, and so he told Elizabeth not to
give away any at all. But there were some Special
People in the village who never had very much to

eat anyway, even when there wasn't a Famine, so
that now there *was* one they were nearly Starving.
So Elizabeth took some of the Palace corn to give
them. (Kings and Queens often seem to feed Poor
People in the winter when there isn't any corn.
Like Joseph did, and Good King Wenceslas did
when he Looked Out and saw a Poor Man Gathering
Winter Fuel.)

Anyway, Elizabeth was carrying some corn in a
big bundle and hoping that no one would see her,
when she suddenly met Queen Sophia and Prince
Ludwig ! Elizabeth was very frightened, because
you remember that she had been told *not* to give any
corn away. So she said to Our Lord :

" Please don't let them see what is in my Bundle,
because then they won't let me have any more, and
those poor people will Die of Hunger."

But Queen Sophia said :

" What have you got there, Elizabeth ? "

" Roses," said Elizabeth.

" *Roses !* " said Queen Sophia. " In the middle
of winter ? I don't believe it ! " And then she
turned to Prince Ludwig and said : " I believe she's
got some of the Palace corn when you said she wasn't
to."

" Oh," said Prince Ludwig, " I am sure she
wouldn't do that. What *have* you got, Elizabeth ? "

Poor Elizabeth was more frightened than ever, so
that she couldn't even speak. Queen Sophia took
hold of her bundle and gave it a Pull to make her
drop it, and Elizabeth let go, and down on to the
Snow tumbled a great bunch of Roses !

Our Lord did quite a lot of other things for Elizabeth, and she spent all her time doing things for Him, and she built a Hospital for all her Ill People, and it is still called the Hospital of St. Elizabeth.

Her Special Day is the 19th of November, and she still has Hospitals built for her.

ST. HUGH OF LINCOLN

ONCE upon a time there lived a little boy called Hugh, and he was six years old. He lived in a house alone with his Mother, because his Father had died such a long time ago that Hugh could not remember him, even though he could remember when he was two.

Well, at that time the Christians and the Un-Christians were horrible to each other, specially the Un-Christians, so horrible that they lived in different parts of the Town ; half for the Christians and half for the Un-Christians, so that they needn't see each other too much. They even had their own special shops and schools, which was very silly because, after all, they were all *People* even if they were Un-Christians and Christians, so they weren't so different as all that. But a funny thing was that the Christians' School was right in the middle of the Un-Christian half of the Town ; I can't think why, because you'd think that they'd have it in their own part. So, when the Christian children went to School they had to go through the Un-Christians' half, and no one liked that very much, but it couldn't be helped.

Hugh, although he was only six, used to go to School and back by himself because his Mother was very poor and couldn't take him because she had a lot of work to do. She used to give him some sandwiches for his dinner and sometimes an apple or a banana as well, done up in a parcel which he carried in his satchel. She always wanted him to put the parcel in last so that it would not get squashed with the books, but Hugh often forgot and put it in first. Usually he had beef sandwiches and honey sandwiches, but on Fridays he had egg ones because, although he did not *hate* fish, he liked egg much better.

At school, before they came home, the children used to have Compline, exactly like we do on Sundays (only, as they didn't go to school on Sundays, they had it on weekdays), and at the end the Bigger Boys used to sing a Latin hymn called " Alma Redemptoris Mater," which means " Kind Mother of our Redeemer." (Redeemer is another name for Our Lord.) Hugh had not got up to doing Latin yet, only the Bigger Boys did it, so he did not know what it meant, but he *loved* the tune and he used to hum it on the way home. Soon he began to know the words because they sang them so often at school, and so he sang them too, and hummed the part he didn't know. One day he asked an Older Boy called Clement, who used to walk home with him sometimes, what the words meant, and Clement, who lived near Hugh's house, told him that they were about Our Lady.

" Is it *all* about Our Lady ? " asked Hugh.

" Yes," said Clement, " it's all about her being God's Mother and how she helps us when we can't do things ourselves."

Hugh was very pleased about this because when he was happy he always wanted to sing very loud, and he did not know any songs about Our Lady. He specially wanted to sing about her when he was going to and from school because he always asked her not to let him get Run Over at the Crossings, and she never did. So Clement taught him the song called " Alma Redemptoris Mater," and Hugh sang it all the way to school and all the way back again, every day, just as loud as he could.

Now the Un-Christians used to hear him singing when he was going through their part of the Town and they hated it because they thought that Our Lady wasn't a bit Special and that she couldn't help anyone, and anyway Hugh was a Christian and they hated Christians. So one day, when Hugh was on his way to school and was going along a very Dark and Narrow Street with bumpy cobble-stones all over it, some of the Un-Christians came out and told him to " Stop singing that silly song because they didn't like it in their part of the Town." But Hugh Knew that Our Lady *was* very Special, so he said :

" No, I won't stop singing, because it is *not* a silly song at all but a song about Our Lady-who-doesn't-let-me-get-run-over-at-crossings, didn't you hear the words ? Besides, she *likes* me singing that song."

This was very brave of Hugh because the Un-Christians were all Grown-up and he was Only Six, but just before he had answered the Un-Christians he had said to Our Lady :

" Would you please tell me something to say, *quick*, so that I needn't stop singing your song ? " And so she did.

Next morning when Hugh came past singing his song, the Un-Christians did a horrible thing. They

caught Hugh when he was Walking along the Dark and Narrow Street and Killed him in the Throat and put him in a deep hole behind their houses !

When he didn't turn up at school that day no one minded because they thought perhaps he had got a cold and was Staying in Bed for Breakfast. And when he was late coming home for Tea his Mother didn't mind either, because *she* thought that he must have gone to have tea with Clement like he often did. So it wasn't till he was late for supper too that she began to wonder Where he Was. So she got supper all ready, and set Hugh's place at the table with his back to the fire in case he was cold coming in late. Then she put on her outdoor things and went to Clement's house to see Clement's Mother about it.

" Is Hugh staying to supper with you as well as tea ? " she asked. " Because it is getting late and it is nearly his bedtime."

" But I haven't seen Hugh all day," said Clement's Mother. " Clement said he thought he must be Staying in Bed for Breakfast as he did not see him at school."

" But he *did* go to school," said Hugh's Mother. " I *know* he did because I remember that he forgot *again* and put his books on top of his sandwiches. I do wish he would not do that, it makes them all squashy."

" What a very Extraordinary Thing ! I think we had better go out and look for him," said Clement's Mother. " Perhaps he has been Run Over at one of those nasty Crossings."

" I don't expect so," said Hugh's Mother, " Because

he always asks Our Lady not to let him be, and she never does."

Anyway, they went out and they looked *every-where* and they couldn't find him. At last they asked some of the Un-Christians, but the Un-Christians were very frightened because they had killed Hugh, and so they said :

" No, we haven't seen him since he came past this morning, singing that silly song of his. Perhaps he has been Kept In at School."

So Hugh's Mother said to Our Lady :

" Do you know where Hugh is ? Because if you do, would you mind telling me, because I'm getting rather bothered, it is so late ? I thought you might know because he sings your Special Song and you don't let him get Run Over at Crossings."

Our Lady did not *say* anything, but just then Hugh's Mother heard him singing " Alma Redemptoris Mater " quite close by. She looked about and found him in the deep hole behind the Un-Christians' houses and singing away like anything. She and Clement's Mother got him out, but they were very surprised that he kept on singing when he was killed, but they were very glad he did or they would never have found him.

When people heard that Hugh was still singing his song after he was dead they were very excited and everybody wanted to see. The Christians were very pleased that God had made Hugh do such a Surprising Thing, but the Un-Christians were very angry because they had been Found Out and would be put in Prison.

Then they took Hugh to the church and the next morning the priest said Mass for him before he was buried, like we always do to people when they die or are killed. But as soon as Mass was finished Hugh

began singing again in the church! So the priest came and said to him :

"Hugh, *why* are you singing when you have been killed? Or aren't you dead at all?"

Then Hugh stopped singing and said :

"Yes, Father, I *am* dead, but God is letting me sing so that everybody will know how Special Our Lady is. She was always my Special Person because she looked after me on the way to school, and when the Un-Christians Killed me in the Throat and put me in a hole, of course my Mother could not find me. So Our Lady came to me and said, ' Sing my Special Song so that your Mother can find you, she has just asked me where you are. And then the Un-Christians will know that I really do look after you.' And then she put a grain of rice under my tongue so that I could sing when I was dead, and when a priest takes it out again she will come back and take me to Heaven with her."

So the priest took the grain from under Hugh's tongue, and he stopped singing, and as soon as he had stopped Our Lady came for him and he went away to Heaven with her, and she looked after his Mother until it was time for her to go to Heaven too.

St. Hugh's Special Day is on the 18th of August, nice and near one of Our Lady's Special Days.

ST. TERESA

ONCE upon a time there was a little girl called Teresa and she lived in the town of Avila in Spain. She was seven years old and her Favourite Thing to Do was reading, and whenever she read about anything she always wanted to go and do it herself. She had eleven brothers and sisters, and one of the brothers, called Rodriguez, loved reading too, but he didn't always want to *do* the things as well. So Teresa and Rodriguez used to read Together whenever they could, and their Favourite Book was about Martyrs, because of the Pictures. It was a very big and heavy book and on every page was a beautiful painted picture. There was one of St. Lawrence being Roasted on a Gridiron for being a Christian, and one of St. Longinus getting Ready for Battle, and one of little St. Hugh walking along the Dark Street in the Un-Christians' Town, and there were heaps of others too.

One day Teresa and Rodriguez were lying on the floor in the nursery with the Big Book when Teresa said :

" I wish *we* could be Martyrs, because then we could go straight to Heaven instead of waiting till we get old and die."

" If you are a Martyr you have to be killed because you are a Christian," said Rodriguez, " and no one will kill *us* because they are Christians themselves."

And he went on looking at a Picture of some Fierce
Lions and some Christian Martyrs with all the Roman
Citizens looking on and cheering and waving flags
and the Band Playing. Really, being a Martyr
must be Most Exciting !

"If we could only get to Morocco the Moors
would chop off our heads *Immediately*," said Teresa ;
"Christians are their Worst Thing."

"It's rather a long way for us to go," said

Rodriguez, who would rather have stayed in the
nursery with the Book.

"Well, will you go if I do ? " asked Teresa.

"I suppose I shall have to," said Rodriguez, who
didn't want Teresa to be a Martyr and get to Heaven
first !

So, after lunch, while they were having their Rest
(and all the Grown-ups were too, because of it being
so hot in Spain), Teresa had a Good Idea.

"Quick ! " she said, "Come on, Rodriguez, before
Nurse comes up from the Kitchen ! "

And they ran out of the nursery and out of the
garden on to the Hot and Dusty Highroad. They

walked and they walked and they walked and they
walked. Rodriguez got tired and dragged his feet,
and the dust flew up in a great cloud and made him
sneeze. He *hated* going to Morocco, but Teresa said
she wasn't tired, and he didn't want her to be a
Martyr and not him.

When their Nurse came up out of the Kitchen and
saw the Children's beds empty she ran to their
Mother, who was still having her Rest.

" Are the children with you, Madam ? " she asked.

" No, Nurse, I thought they were with you," said
their Mother, and they started looking All Over the
House.

" You look upstairs and I'll look downstairs," said
the Mother, and she looked in the Hall and in the
Dining-room and in the Library and behind the
Drawing-room sofa and under the Kitchen table.
No one there !

" Bother the children ! " said the Children's Mother.

Nurse looked under all the beds, in the Bath, in
the Wardrobes and on top of the cupboard in the
Nursery. No one there !

" Oh ! deary, deary, what *has* become of them ? "
said Nurse.

" The only thing to do," said their Mother, " is to
wait until Uncle Juan comes Home in Time for Tea,
and then he can go out on his Swift Horse and find
them." And they started getting Tea ready so that
Uncle Juan would not have to wait.

When Uncle Juan was riding along on the Swift
Horse so as to be Home in Time for Tea he saw a
Cloud of Dust coming along the road to meet him !

" Dear me," he thought, " I do hope it isn't Moors, they might cut off my head." So he rode his horse into a field and hid behind a hedge and waited for the Cloud of Dust to go past in case there were Moors in it.

As it came nearer and nearer, Uncle Juan said to himself : " It looks rather small for Moors, perhaps it's a Wolf ! " So he waited some more. He wasn't actually *frightened*, but he hadn't got his Sharp Sword with him, and its Absence might have led to Awkward Complications.

When the Cloud of Dust came up to him a Voice came out of it ! Uncle Juan got such a fright that he nearly jumped Right Out of his skin. He just managed to keep inside it by pressing down the top of his head.

This is what the Voice said :

" *Need* we be Martyrs *to-day*, Teresa ? Couldn't we p'raps be them to-morrow instead ? "

And there were Rodriguez and Teresa still walking along the Hot and Dusty Highroad !

" What *are* you two doing here all alone ? " asked Uncle Juan.

" We're being Martyrs," said poor Rodriguez sadly.

" No, *going* to be Martyrs," said Teresa, "in Morocco. Our heads'll be cut off and then we'll be in Heaven. We're walking there."

" But what about the sea ? " asked Uncle Juan. " How will you get across ? "

" *Is* there any sea ? " said Teresa. " I never knew that. *Bother !* Well, we can be Hermits in the garden instead." (Hermits are people who live all alone in little huts and sometimes turn into Saints.)

Rodriguez was very pleased that the sea was in the way. He had not really wanted to be a Martyr, but only because Teresa did.

" Can I ride on your horse, going home ? " he said.

" Can *I* ? " said Teresa.

So Uncle Juan put Rodriguez up on the saddle in

front of him and Teresa up behind him and they trotted home grandly on the Swift Horse.

Their Mother was Rather Cross when they got home, but when they told her about being Martyrs she said it was an Excellent Plan but Impracticable, and being Hermits was the Same Thing, only Better.

So after Tea they went out into the garden to build Hermits' Cells, but whenever the walls got a little bit high they fell down again and Rodriguez said Hermits was a Silly Idea and he would rather be a Soldier when he grew up. And when he did grow up he *was* a Very Fine Soldier who went to fight in South America, but Teresa invented a New Kind of Nun. And this is how she did it.

There were already some nuns and friars who dressed in brown, with white cloaks. They were called Carmelites, after Our Lady of Mount Carmel. Teresa liked the Carmelites because a lot of Hermits lived on Mount Carmel, and she still *rather* wanted to be a Hermit. But she thought that they ought to be Sterner and Poorer. So she didn't let her sort of Carmelite have any Stockings and made them have Harder Rules to keep.

So if any of you live near a Carmelite Church or Convent and you see the Fathers dressed in brown and white you can remember about Teresa and the Stockings.

St. Teresa's Special Day is on October 15th, and I expect lots of people's Birthdays are on that day.

ST. ALOYSIUS GONZAGA

ONCE upon a time there was a little boy called Aloysius whose Father was a Marquis and a Soldier.

On his Fourth Birthday his Father gave him a Whole Army of tin soldiers, with their Swords and their Tents and their Cavalry and their Infantry and their Cannon and their Gun-carriages and their Different Regiments. Like Hussars and Dragoons and London Scottish and the Grenadiers. (Only they weren't really those actual Regiments because the Gonzagas were Italian, so they had Italian regiments.)

The Cannon really Worked. I mean they were made like real Cannon and they had tiny Cannon-balls which knocked over the soldiers, but they didn't really explode in case Aloysius hurt himself, because he was Only Four.

Aloysius *loved* his Army. He used to have Battles all day long all over the Nursery floor. He used to divide them in half and have one half for the Enemy, and His Side always won because the Enemy had no one to fire off their Cannon for them.

Aloysius got so good at making Battles that his father the Marquis said that he would take him with him when he was Five, to gather together a Real Army to fight with the Tunisians.

So, on his Fifth Birthday, Aloysius began to ask his Mother if he could go yet? Now his Mother did

not want him to go away, with only the soldiers to
Look After him and Bath him and Cut up his Dinner,
so she always said :

" Not yet, Darling, wait till your Father sends for
you." Because she hoped that his Father would
forget. And every day Aloysius asked her the same
thing, and every day she answered the same thing.

At last, one evening, just when Aloysius had gone
to bed, the Marquis came Home.

" Where's Aloysius ? " he shouted, " I want him,"

and he Stamped About with his sword clanking on his
Armour and all the ornaments on the mantel-piece
shook and rattled.

" Hush, dear, don't make such a noise," said
Aloysius' mother, " he's gone to bed, you'll wake him
up ! "

" I can't help that," said the Marquis, who was a
man of Stern Qualities, " I really must see him
now ! " And he Stamped About some more.

So Aloysius came downstairs in his dressing-gown
and bedroom-slippers and his hair all untidy, to see
why his Father wanted him.

"There, my boy!" said the Marquis, very loud,
"what do you think of that, eh?" And he showed
Aloysius a very Big Parcel. His Mother helped him
to undo the string, and there, inside, was a little suit
of Armour, just the right size for him, and a Helmet
to match. Aloysius was so Enraptured that he did

not know what to do next! He put on the Armour
and the Helmet and then he ran about the room,
and made noises like a Bugle and a Drum, until his
mother said he was getting Too Excited and he
Really Must Go Back to Bed. Aloysius didn't want
to go a bit, but his father said very loud:

"Now, my boy, Orders are Orders in the Army!
Up you go!" So he had to.

Next day the Marquis went away to gather together
the Army to fight the Tunisians, and Aloysius went
too!

The first thing Aloysius did when he found himself alone at the Barracks (a Barracks is a big place where soldiers live) was to find an Arquebus, which is an old sort of gun, and to Fire it Off! He didn't know that it would fire backwards too, his toy ones didn't, and he burnt off all his hair and eyebrows, and his face was covered with black Gunpowder and he looked like a Bald-headed Golliwog! The soldiers all laughed at him, but the Marquis wasn't at all pleased, because he said the Child Might have Killed Some-one! So Aloysius left the Arquebuses alone after that.

One day, all the soldiers were having their After-dinner Rest, and Aloysius was too. But he got tired of lying down, so he got up and wandered about the Barracks Square where the Cannon were, with their piles of Cannon-balls beside them.

"Well, how funny!" he thought, "these guns look just like the ones in *my* Army! I wonder if they load the same way?"

The Cannon-balls were very heavy and Aloysius nearly couldn't lift one, but at last he managed to load the Cannon.

"I wonder if it Fires Off the same as my ones?" he thought, and he tried to see if it would. It did! There was an Enormous Explosion and Aloysius was knocked over backwards and rolled under the gun-carriage.

When he felt a little better he looked out through the wheels and saw all the soldiers lining up and the officers putting on their swords and the Marquis shouting orders and the sentries running about and

Everything all very Hurried and Exciting! Suddenly the Marquis looked across the Barracks Square and saw Aloysius' Cannon still smoking! He rode up and saw Aloysius hiding underneath! He pulled him out, and in a Terrible Voice asked him what had happened. Aloysius told him, and the Marquis was very Roaring and Angry and said he must be Punished very Severely for giving them all such a Fright. They had thought that the Enemy had Suddenly

Attacked them! But all the soldiers, who thought it was very Funny, asked if he might be let off, so he was. But the Marquis said he Couldn't Possibly have him at the Barracks any more, and he was sent home, but he talked like the soldiers, very Loud and Ordery, and his mother was shocked.

Aloysius then lived at Home until he was old enough to be a Marquis and a soldier like his Father, but when he was Grown-up he became a different sort of soldier, and this was the sort:

Did you know that the Pope had an Army? Well, he has; a proper Army with a proper General. Most of the Soldiers in it are Priests as well. And the Pope sends them out to All the Countries in the

World to fight for Christ the King against Satan and Heresies and Paganism and Heathenism, which are all very long words for things that hurt Our Lord very badly. So you see why these Soldiers have to be Priests as well, because, if they happen to be fighting in a country that is on Satan's Side and some of the people suddenly want to Change Sides, well, there is a Priest all ready to tell them about it! These Soldier-Priests are always being Killed by their Enemies, but one of their rules is that *they* are not allowed to kill their Enemies in case God is not quite ready for them yet. The name of the Pope's regiment or Army isn't the Coldstream Guards or the East Yorkshires or something, but the Society of Jesus. And the Priest-Soldiers are called Jesuits and they are Very Brave Men.

So when he was eighteen Aloysius became a Jesuit, and he loved God so much, and did so much for Him, that when he was twenty-three God let him go to Heaven so as to be nearer to Him, instead of having to wait until he was an old man. If he hadn't gone to Heaven so soon, people thought that he would have ended by being a General, he was so good at being a soldier. But Aloysius was glad, and went one morning just after having had Holy Communion.

St. Aloysius Gonzaga's Special Day is June the 21st, and if anybody is called Louis or Lewis or Louisa or Louise, then it is their Special day, too; specially if it is their Birthday.

BARNABAS OF COMPIEGNE

ONCE upon a time there was a dear little man called Barnabas. He was frightfully good at playing a Special Game with balls and knives called Juggling. He dressed in a very funny way, too. Everything was blue or white (you will see why in a minute). One shoe was blue and the other white, and so were his stockings and sleeves. His hat was white, and he had a blue handkerchief, and he had little golden bells on his sleeves so that they tinkled when he was juggling. There were six copper balls and twelve sharp shiny knives, and he used to throw them all up in the air and catch them, and he never dropped a ball or cut his fingers. He was so clever at being a juggler that people used to give him pennies to see him do it, so he used to go from town to town collecting his pennies and humming to himself, and being very happy, except when it rained. When it rained the balls and knives were slippery, and then he did drop them sometimes, and people thought he wasn't a bit clever, and wouldn't give him pennies. So he was nearly always hungry on wet days.

His Very Special Person was Our Lady (so *now* you see why he dressed in blue and white, don't you?), and every time he passed a church he used to go in and ask her to look after him and not let it rain too often.

One wet day he was walking along looking for a

barn to sleep in when he caught up with a monk, and they walked along together.

" Why do you have to dress like that ? Are you a clown ? " asked the monk.

" I don't *have* to, and I am *not* a clown," said Barnabas. " I am Barnabas the Juggler. To be a juggler is the Grandest Thing in the World."

" Oh, no," said the monk, " it may be a very nice thing to be, but it isn't as Special and Important as being a monk, because monks live with God and Our Lady as much as they can."

" I wish *I* could do that ! " said Barnabas. " Our Lady is my Special Person. Can I come and be a monk with you ? "

" Yes," said the monk. " As it happens, it is very lucky you asked me that, because I am the Prior of that monastery over there. Come and be a monk with us ! "

So Barnabas went to be a monk with the Prior, and

he dressed in black instead of blue and white, which was rather sad for him, but he didn't mind *very* much.

In this monastery all the Brothers had a Special Thing to do for Our Lady.

The Prior wrote very clever books about her. Brother Maurice painted beautiful little pictures of her for the books, in red and blue and gold. Brother Denis grew special lilies in the garden for her altar. Brother Marbode used to make marble statues. His black clothes were always covered with little chips of marble, and his hair was all dusty. His Most Important statue was a beautiful one of Our Lady that stood in the chapel. She had a crown on and the little Baby Jesus was asleep on her shoulder, and Barnabas (or Brother Barnabas, now he was a monk) used to go and look at this statue and feel *very* sad, because all the monks could do something very clever for Our Lady except himself. And he couldn't do *anything* nicely except juggle. So he got sadder and sadder, and the Prior thought perhaps he didn't like being a monk after all.

One day, before it was time to get up, he had a Beautiful Idea. He jumped up and ran quickly to the chapel before any of the others got there. After dinner he went again, *and* after tea. Each time he came back so happy that the Prior couldn't *think* what he had been doing, because usually he was rather sad. So, after supper, when Brother Barnabas had gone to the chapel *again*, the Prior and Brother Maurice (who painted the pictures) followed him and looked through the door to see what he was doing. And what do you suppose he *was* doing? Well, he was standing on his

head and juggling with his six copper balls and twelve
shiny knives, *right* in front of Our Lady's Altar !

You see, it was the *only* clever thing he could do,

so he did it for Our Lady and hoped she wouldn't
mind.

The Prior and Brother Maurice (who painted the
pictures) were so surprised that they just stood and
stared for a minute. Then the Prior said :

" Poor Brother Barnabas must have gone mad !
Quick, go and tell Brother Marbode (who makes
statues) to help us to get him out. It is a Calamitous
Thing to do things like that in the chapel ! "

They were just going to go in to take Brother

Barnabas away when he stopped juggling and knelt in front of the statue that Brother Marbode had made of Our Lady, and looked at it. Then they saw her come down from the Altar and wipe Barnabas' hot forehead and smile at him ! *She* knew he wasn't at all mad, and she loved him doing his juggling for her, because it was the only Special Thing he knew. So the Prior and the Brothers went quietly away, and Barnabas never saw them.

After that the Prior let Brother Barnabas do it always, and never told him that he knew what the Beautiful Idea was, because it would have spoilt it all. It was Brother Barnabas' Own Special Secret.

BERNADETTE OF LOURDES

Once upon a time there was a little girl who had an Aunt called Aunt Bernarde. So her Mother called her Bernadette, which means Little Bernarde, after the Aunt. (Just like Cigar*ette* means Little Cigar, and Kitchen*ette* means Little Kitchen.)

Bernadette lived with her mother and her father and her sister, whose name was 'Toinette (which means Little Antony, after St. Francis' friend). They were very, very poor, and had only one room in their house, and Bernadette always had a Bad Cough.

Well, one morning, after breakfast, Bernadette noticed that there was no more wood for the fire (it was a very cold day in February), and she said to her mother :

" Shall I go out and find some more wood ? Or we won't be able to cook the dinner."

And her mother said :

" Thank you, dear, but I'll go because of your Cough. It is too cold for you."

Just when they were settling who should go, there came a knock at the door : Rat ! tat ! tat !

" Come in ! " said Bernadette's mother, and a little girl called Jeanne (French for Joan) came in with her baby brother, who was Only Two, to play with 'Toinette.

" Let's *all* go and find some wood. I know a Special Place," said 'Toinette, who didn't want to stay indoors because she would have to help to wash up the breakfast things. So they all went out with a big basket, and Bernadette took some lozenges for her Cough. On the way to 'Toinette's Special Place they left Jeanne's little brother at his house, because he was such a bother and wanted to be carried.

'Toinette's Special Place was the other side of a stream, where there wasn't a bridge, and just across the stream was a big Cave with a big Rock beside it. 'Toinette and Jeanne paddled across, and the water

was so cold that their feet nearly froze and made them cry. Bernadette daren't cross. It was so cold, and besides, she had a Cough. She tried to find some stepping-stones, but she couldn't. The others went farther and farther away, picking up sticks, and soon poor Bernadette was Left Alone.

It *was* so cold ! Bernadette looked across the stream and thought :

" If only I could go in that Cave the wind mightn't be so cold."

She went to the edge of the stream and began to take off her shoes, but she coughed so much that she couldn't balance on one foot while she unfastened the other. So *she* began to cry, too ! Then she thought she would say her Rosary until the others came back. So she knelt down, but her fingers were so cold that she couldn't feel the beads, and she had to look all the time to see where she had got up to. After a little while she looked up to see if 'Toinette and Jeanne were coming back yet, and there, right in front of her, was the Most Surprising Thing that had ever happened to her !

Right on top of the big rock by the cave there stood a Beautiful Lady ! She wasn't holding on, and the wind wasn't blowing her things about like it was Bernadette's. She smiled. Bernadette rubbed her eyes and looked again. How *could* the Lady have climbed up there without her noticing ? And who could she be ? She had on a long white dress, and a blue sash, and a white veil over her hair, and she was holding a gold Rosary with white beads. It looked as if she was saying it with Bernadette. When she saw the Rosary, Bernadette remembered that she had stopped in the middle of hers, and she thought that perhaps the Lady had come to say it with her. Only why did she stand in such a funny place ? Why didn't she come and kneel with Bernadette ? The Lady smiled at her again, and she suddenly felt quite warm and happy instead of cold and miserable. She forgot that 'Toinette and Jeanne had Left her Behind, so she went on saying her Rosary, and the Lady looked as if she were saying it too, but Bernadette only heard her saying the " Our Father " and the " Glory be " parts.

" What *are* you doing ? What are you saying your prayers out here for ? " said a voice behind her. Bernadette jumped. The others had come back without her noticing them.

" What are you looking at ? Why are you looking so pleased ? *I* can't see anything," said Jeanne.

" Look at that Lady up on the Rock," said Bernadette. " Who is she ? "

" There isn't anybody, you've been asleep, Lazy, while we've been picking up the sticks," said 'Toinette. " Come along home, my feet are cold."

When they got home, 'Toinette told her mother what Bernadette had been doing, and her mother said it was a Dream. But it wasn't.

Next day Bernadette said she was going to the cave again to see if the Lady would come back. Aunt Bernarde and her mother said that they would go too. So they started off. Now, to get to the stream they had to go down a very steep and narrow and stony path. Bernadette could run down it, but Aunt Bernarde and her mother had to hold on to the side and go down slowly.

" I was saying my Rosary last time," said Bernadette when they had caught her up. " I think I had better say it again this time."

So she knelt down in the muddy field, near the edge of the stream.

" There she is ! " she said.

But Aunt Bernarde and the mother couldn't see anyone. Bernadette thought this was very funny, but she didn't bother much because she was hoping that the Lady would tell her who she was.

" Would you please tell me who you are ? " asked Bernadette. She was rather frightened, but her mother and Aunt Bernarde kept on whispering to her to ask. Besides, the Lady looked very kind, so perhaps she wouldn't mind being asked.

" I want you to come here, to see me, every day for a fortnight," said the Lady, " and then I'll tell you something Very Important." Then she disappeared.

Aunt Bernarde and Bernadette's mother were Rather Cross because they had not seen the Lady, so when Bernadette told her mother what the Lady had said about going there every day for a fortnight, she said :

" Of *course* you can't come here every day ! It is much too cold, and your Cough will get worse. You are a very Naughty Little Girl, pretending to see a Lady like that, and making Aunt Bernarde and me come all the way down that steep path for nothing ! "

Poor Bernadette cried again ! It wasn't fair of people, and she couldn't think why no one else saw the Lady when there she was, all the time, as plain as plain. But she did wish the Lady had said who she was, because *everyone* said :

" Who *is* she, Bernadette ? " and when she said, " I don't know," they *always* said, " Well, then, it can't be anyone at all." Which was silly of them, because you often see people without knowing who they are.

When Bernadette's father heard about it he was sorry for her, and he said :

" Well, I don't see why she shouldn't go, if she puts her shawl on, and doesn't make her Cough worse."

So every day Bernadette tidied up the Room that was the Whole House ; put some more wood on the fire ; swept up the floor ; put on her shawl ; and went out down the very steep path to the stream in front of the Cave. And every day more and more people followed her to see what would happen, until there were Crowds and Crowds ; but none of them ever saw the Lady except Bernadette. But they went on going because they hoped they might, although they thought that Bernadette was Only Pretending all the time.

One of the days, when Bernadette was kneeling by the stream, the Lady came and said :

" Cross the stream and come into the Cave, I want to tell you something."

Bernadette crossed the stream (it didn't feel a bit cold after all) and went in, and the Lady said :

" Kneel on the ground." Bernadette knelt down and waited to see what would happen next.

" Dig a little hole in the ground with your fingers," said the Lady, " and you will see something Surprising."

Bernadette scratched up the ground and made a little hole. She stopped and looked at it, and saw that it filled itself with water !

" Make it a little bigger," said the Lady. Bernadette did. More water came, and made the hole Brimful. More came, and the hole Overflowed and began to trickle along the floor of the Cave towards the field outside.

" Now wash in it," said the Lady. Bernadette washed her face and hands, and found that it did not make her a bit cold. She suddenly felt very well and happy, and her Cough stopped making her chest hurt.

Now, all the people waiting outside couldn't think *what* Bernadette was doing in the Cave all this time, and they were getting Rather Cross, waiting in the cold, when suddenly someone said :

" Look ! " They all looked and they saw the water coming out of the Cave like a very thin stream. As they looked it got bigger and bigger, and wider and wider, until it was a very wide one flowing across the field into the other stream.   (The one that Bernadette didn't dare to cross the first day she saw the Lady.) Everyone was looking at the New Stream when Bernadette came out of the Cave.   She didn't notice them, and went straight home.   She didn't tell anyone how the New Stream came, or what the Lady had said to her.

That evening, when they were having supper, there came another knock at the door : Rat ! tat ! tat !

" Come in ! " said Aunt Bernarde, and Fifteen people came in ! Outside the door there were about Twenty more !

" Oh dear ! " said Bernadette's mother.   " What *do* they all want ? We haven't got enough chairs ! Here, Bernadette ! 'Toinette ! Get up and give your chairs to the ladies ! What are you thinking about ? Where are your manners ? "

But Bernadette and 'Toinette had been sitting with their mouths open, they were so Surprised ! *Never* had they had so many visitors ! Not even at Easter, when everybody went and visited everybody else.

" We want to know," said a Fat Lady with a Red Face, " what the Lady said to Bernadette in the Cave when she made the New Stream." She sat down very hard on 'Toinette's chair, and one of the legs cracked.

" *Do* be careful," said Bernadette's mother, " that chair isn't very strong ! "

" It's strong enough for *me*," said the Fat Red Lady, putting her hat straight. " Now Bernadette ! Tell us *all* about it ! "

" I can't tell you *anything*," said poor Bernadette, " except that she said that everybody must do penance because they aren't good enough, and that they must come and pray by the New Stream. She wants us to build a Church there, to pray in."

" Is *that* all ? " said a Thin Cross Lady with a Sharp Nose. " We knew the Penance part before, we have it in Sermons ! Catch *me* praying in a nasty damp field ; getting my death of cold ! "

" *And* building a Church, above all ! " said a Stout Man with grey hair and a Gold Watch Chain. " Where are they going to get the money from, I'd like to know ? *I* can't give anything ! "

" She told me something else, very Special and Important," said Bernadette, " but she said that I mustn't tell anybody."

Of course everybody tried to find out what the Special and Important thing was, and they were all Very Angry when Bernadette wouldn't tell them.

The next day the Priest told Bernadette that she really *must* ask the Lady again who she was. Because how could they build her a Church when they did not know whom they were building it for ? So everyone went down the steep path to see if, perhaps, they could *hear* the Lady, even if they couldn't *see* her.

They found some Ill People already there, who had heard about Bernadette's Cough being much better. They had been washing themselves in the New Stream, and some of them got quite better at once.

After Bernadette had been saying her Rosary for a little while the Lady came, as usual, to the top of the Rock. Bernadette suddenly felt Very Brave, and, looking up at the Lady, she said :

" Would you mind very much if you told me who you are ? Everybody keeps *on* asking me, and I never know what to say." But the Lady only smiled.

" *Please* tell me," said Bernadette. But the Lady only smiled again, and she didn't answer.

" Dear Lady, do tell me ! " said Bernadette. Then the Lady said, very quietly :

" I am the Immaculate Conception." And she disappeared.

Now Bernadette did not know what this meant at all. So she went to the priest and told him what the Lady had said, and asked him if *he* knew. The priest did, and he was very sorry he had not believed Bernadette before. Because " The Immaculate Conception " is another, and very long, name for Our Lady ! And there she had been, all the time, every day for a fortnight, and everybody could have gone to love her and pray to her, and they hadn't even *seen* her, because they hadn't believed it *could* be, and they had said that Bernadette was Only Pretending all the time.

(*Now* do you see why the Lady didn't say the " Hail Mary " part of the Rosary ? Because then she'd have been talking to herself, wouldn't she ?)

Then the priest said :

" Now, Bernadette, you *simply must* tell me what Our Lady said to you, because it is very Important for me to Know. The Bishop will ask me."

But Bernadette said :

" I am very sorry, Father, but I can't tell you. She said I *mustn't* tell anyone."

" But," said the priest, " supposing the Pope asked you, you'd *have* to tell *him*."

" I wouldn't have to," said Bernadette, " because she said not to tell *any* one, and the Pope *is* someone."

So no one ever knew what Bernadette's Special Important Secret was.

Well, people still go to pray at the Church by the Rock (because they did build one after all), and heaps and crowds of people from All Over the World go and wash in the New Stream, and lots of them get better. You have heard of people going to Lourdes, haven't you ? Well, that is where the New Stream is. Our Lady still goes there, too, but she doesn't let people see her any more. The only one who ever saw her was Bernadette. Perhaps no one else was nice enough to be allowed to.

St. Bernadette's Special Day is April 16th. She hasn't had it very long so I don't expect many people are

called after her yet.   Of course, there is another very
Important Day belonging to this story.   Whose do

you suppose ? Our Lady of Lourdes, of course, on
February 11th, the day that Bernadette first saw her.

ANNE DE GUIGNE

THIS is a story about a little girl called Anne who used to live with her Mother in France. Now she lives in Heaven and helps people quite a lot, but her mother still lives at their home with all her other children.

Well, when Anne was Four her father was killed in the War, like lots of people's fathers were, and her mother was so sad that Anne cried, she was so sorry for her.

" Why was he killed ? Do you know, Mummy ? " she asked.

" He gave his life so that we should be safe," said her mother. " It was a Sacrifice. If our soldiers didn't go and fight and be killed, the enemy would come and Take us all Prisoners."

That made Anne think of the great Sacrifice that Our Lord made for us when He was Crucified. A Sacrifice is when you give something you like to somebody else. And the more you like the thing, the bigger the Sacrifice. Our Lord's was a very Special Sacrifice because He was killed in a very Horrible Way so that we could go to Heaven. And He *needn't* have done it like that because He is God and could have done it in a way much nicer for Himself. Or He needn't have Bothered about us at all, but just had Heaven all nice for Himself and His Angels. But He wanted us to be His Special People because He loves us, so He made the biggest Sacrifice

He could and let the Jews scourge Him and bully Him and then crucify Him. He needn't *even* have come and been a Man, because that wasn't very nice for God, was it, if you think of it ?

Anyway, Anne suddenly thought that if Our Lord had sacrificed so much for her, she ought to do something back. We always want to do something nice for people who do nice things for us, don't we ?

" I can't give Him a Sacrifice like He gave me," she said to herself, " but if I do lots and lots of little ones perhaps they will Add Up into One Big One."

So, when she remembered, she used to do things for Our Lord. If she bumped her head on the corner of the table she used to say that Our Lord could have it in return for what He had given her ; or if her brother Jacques took away her Special toy Wheelbarrow *just* when she was going to use it, she used to give it up to him so as to add to her Secret Store of Sacrifices. Or if chocolates were handed round she used to try and be forgotten, and all sorts of things like that. And she remembered more and more as she got older so that by the time she was Nine she was doing them all the time, only she didn't Tell Anybody what she was doing.

You know if you are told to do something you often don't want to do it ? But if you like the person who tells you to, you *like* doing it ? Well, Anne loved Our Lord, and because she *really* loved Him (like you love Mummy) and kept on doing things for Him to add to her Sacrifices, He used to talk to her. When she went to Holy Communion He told her all sorts of things, and He did everything that she asked Him to. Her Special Thing to Do, when she wasn't playing in the Nursery or doing Lessons, was to find out about someone who Stole things, or who wouldn't ever go to Church or something. Then she would tell Our Lord about it and ask Him to make it all right. Then she would run and ask someone :

" Has he stopped stealing yet ? " and, if he hadn't, she said :

" Well, I'll go and pray some more, and then he will." And she did pray, and he did stop, always ! Because Our Lord always does extra things for the people who do things for Him.

One thing that Our Lord told Anne was His Favourite Word. What do you suppose it was ? Everybody knows it. Guess ! It is quite a short one. It is " Yes." It is a funny one to have for a favourite, isn't it ? The thing is, you see, whatever anyone says, or wants you to do, you say " Yes." Even if you Hate doing it. The more you hate it the bigger your sacrifice to add to your Special Pile of Sacrifices. And Our Lord or your Guardian Angel counts each time you say it, and at the end we'll all see who has the most.

Well, by the time she was Ten Anne had got quite a lot of people to remember to love God by praying for them, and she got so good at it that God thought she'd be better in Heaven, nearer Him. And then she'd be able to get still more people, because everybody would know where she was and could ask her to do things for them more easily. So one day she had a very bad Headache. Anne was pleased about that because she said she liked being like Our Lord and His Crown of Thorns. But the headache got much worse and after a few days Our Lady came and took her away to Heaven.

When she had been there about a week, an old man in the village near her home got very ill. Anne's mother went to see him. He knew that he was dying, but he said that he didn't like God, he never *had* liked Him, and he wasn't *going* to like Him, however much He had done for him, so there !

" Oh dear ! " thought Anne's mother, " I wish Anne was here. It is *just* the sort of thing she could have asked Our Lord about."

Then she thought :

" Well, after all, Anne is still my little girl, even if she has gone to Heaven, and she must do as she is told." So she said, " Anne, you really *must* see about this old man. Ask Our Lord to make him sensible before he dies."

And the old man turned over in bed and said :

" Well, after all, I was Stupid about not liking God, and I am sorry I said all that."

Hadn't Anne been quick about it ?

Then Everybody began to ask Anne to do things for them, just like they used to while she was at home, and she still does because she has never forgotten Our Lord's favourite word.

Not very long ago Anne's sister Marinette got " flu," and was Very Ill in Bed with a Temperature. Anne's mother and the Doctor thought that she was going to die. So they asked Anne to ask Our Lord not to take Marinette away too, if He didn't mind, because it would be so lonely without her. As soon as they had finished asking, Marinette sat up and said she felt hungry and was Much Better, Thank you ! Anne had said " Yes " again.

Now, there is one thing that you mightn't know

about when you start Collecting Unselfishnesses, and it is this : Did you know that there is a sort of Un-selfishness that is Selfish? I know it sounds all wrong, but it is when people Grab *all* the Not Very Nice things to do, and that doesn't give anyone else a chance of being Unselfish too. They might be collecting " Yes's " just as hard as you are, and you are spoiling it for them !

Anne hasn't got a Special Day yet, but her Mother is collecting all the things that she does from Heaven, and when she has got enough she will send them to the Pope, and then perhaps he will say which day she can have.   So anyone called Anne can have Our Lady's Mother's Special Day, because she was Anne too ; it is July 26th.

ST. MICHAEL

ONCE upon a time, right at the Very Beginning of Things, there was a Battle in Heaven, and this is how it happened:

God had made Heaven and all the Angels and all the extra Important Angels called Archangels. (Like an extra important Bishop is called an Archbishop.) The Archangels were God's very Special Friends, and were Shining and Strong and Powerful. One was called Gabriel. He was the one that God sent to tell Our Lady about being the Mother of God. Another was called Raphael. He was the one who helped Tobias in the Bible. Another was called Michael. He was " the Angel of the Lord," who was sent to Moses and Jacob and Abraham and people. Another was Lucifer, who was so beautiful that the other Angels called him the Son of the Morning.

Well, everybody was very happy because they could see God, and they all loved Him because he had made them so Strong and Shining and Lovely.

Then one day Lucifer, Son of the Morning, said to himself: " Why should God be the Most Important Person in Heaven? Why shouldn't *I* be? I can fly and I can change into other things, and I am beautiful and I am powerful. In Fact, I am *just* as Important as God, and I shan't do what He tells me ever again. I shall fight Him and have Heaven for Mine ! "

This was really very Stupid of Lucifer, wasn't it ? Because he wouldn't have been there at all if God hadn't made him, so of Course he wasn't so Important. Also he was being Vain and Proud and Treacherous, which is Plotting against the King.

So Lucifer went round Heaven and he collected a lot of other Angels who didn't want to be less Important than God, until he had a Great Army.

Then they marched up to the Throne of God and said Proudly :

" We are just as Important as You. Why should *You* be the King of Heaven any more than one of us ? We are Strong and Proud and Beautiful, and we will Fight You for the Kingdom of Heaven."

God looked at them. Then He said :

" Lucifer, I thought that you were My Friend and I trusted you. Be sensible, now, and *think* what you are doing."

" I *have* thought," said Lucifer, " and I'd rather not be in Heaven at all than have You for my King, and so would all of us ! "

And behind him all the Rebel Angels shouted with a great shout :

" We will follow Lucifer ! Long live Lucifer ! Let *him* reign over us in Heaven ! WE DO NOT WANT GOD ! "

" Very well," said God, " if you don't want Me, you needn't have Me. But if you want to fight for Heaven, you can if you think it will be any good."

And He called Michael the Archangel and made him gather together a Mighty Army of Angels who were on God's side.

Then there was a Great Battle in Heaven, Michael and his Angels fighting with Lucifer ; and Lucifer fought ; and *his* angels ; but they did not win. And Michael drove him Right Out of Heaven and he fell down, and down, and down to Hell, and all his angels were driven down after him, and, as the last one disappeared from sight for ever and the Gate of Heaven clanged shut, a great Shout went up from Michael's Army :

" Heaven has won ! Rejoice and be glad all you Angels ! The Good God always wins ! "

So now you know why we sometimes say in our prayers, " Holy Michael the Archangel, defend us in the Day of Battle," because he is so good at battles.

But what happened to Lucifer and his Rebel Angels ? Well, he was so Furious and Enraged at having lost his Battle with God that he has never got over it. You see, he is never allowed inside Heaven any more for ever and ever and ever, and now that he *can't* go he is angry about it. So, in Revenge, he does everything horrible to God that he can. His Worst Feeling is Jealousy, Who do you suppose he is jealous of ? *Us !* Why ? Because when Our Lord was Crucified He opened the Kingdom of Heaven for *us* to go in ! So Lucifer, whose other name is Satan, or the Devil, is *Furious* because we Ordinary People are allowed in, and *he*, an Archangel, isn't. So he and his angels try always and always to stop us going in by giving us bad Ideas, and making us do things that we Know are wrong so as to hurt God. So whenever you want to do or say something horrid, think of the Great Battle in Heaven, and remember that it is Lucifer trying to keep you on his side. If you don't do or say it, you have won and have stayed on God's side.

St. Michael's Special Day is September 29th, and it is called the Feast of St. Michael and All Angels because of all the Angels who helped him in the Battle.